CW00547865
WITHDRAWN FROM
30127 08813580 6

THIS ENCHANTING BOOK
ON BIRDS AND BEASTS
BELONGS TO

....

BIRDS AND BEASTS

ENCHANTING TALES OF INDIA

A Retelling

FOREWORD BY

SONALI BENDRE BEHL

Editor Ayushi Thapliyal
Art Editor, Illustrator, and Jacket Designer Priyal Mote

Senior DTP Designer Jagtar Singh
DTP Designer Ashok Kumar
Pre-production Manager Narender Kumar

Managing Editor Chitra Subramanyam
Managing Art Editor Neha Ahuja Chowdhry

Managing Director, India Aparna Sharma

Retold by Ayushi Thapliyal, Chitra Subramanyam, Nayan Keshan, Arushi Mathur, Bipasha Roy, Priyanka Kharbanda, Rishi Bryan, Sukriti Kapoor, Upamanyu Das

Proofreaders Vatsal Verma, Hina Jain

First published in Great Britain in 2020
by Dorling Kindersley Limited
One Embassy Gardens, 8 Viaduct Gardens,
London, SW11 7BW

10 9 8 7 6 5 4 3 2 1
001-322201-Nov/2020

A CIP catalogue record for this book
is available from the British Library.
ISBN: 978-0-2414-7194-4

Printed in India

For the curious
www.dk.com

Foreword

Our stories make us who we are.

Storytelling has been such an integral part of society and culture. With stories passed down from generation to generation, to the stories our grandparents tell us, and the ones we tell our kids at bedtime. Stories with moral values, about the origin of how the world was created, the ones of kings and kingdoms, gods and goddesses – they have strengthened familial bonds, taught us lessons, and shaped our personalities. India is a treasure trove of these tales, some well-known and others hidden gems. This book endeavours to highlight those stories in a compilation of folk tales and folklore of animals, monsters, and birds. It is also an attempt to preserve cultural beliefs and tribal folklore, which are quickly being forgotten.

What I love about *Birds and Beasts: Enchanting Tales of India – A Retelling* is that the stories are magical and mystical, and they have been beautifully illustrated. A delight to read, the book opens our eyes to stories sourced from all across India, from the Khasi people in the northeast to the Lingayat community of Karnataka. It also includes stories from ancient texts, such as the *Ramayana, Mahabharata, Hitopadesha* and more, as well as those recorded by the British.

With this, let's remember the diverse beliefs, cultures, and traditions that make India so beautiful and vibrant.

With this, let's remember who we are.

Sonali Bendre Behl

Actor, Author, Bibliophile, and Founder of Sonali's Book Club

Contents

How Butterflies were Born

A myth from the Parenga tribe of Odisha

Sitiyadai, the young daughter of Lakshmi, the goddess of prosperity and wealth, stepped out of her home, closed her eyes, and took a deep breath. The white flowers were in full bloom, like little stars in a sea of green, and their intoxicating fragrance enveloped her.

"You are the real queen of the night. You are too pretty to be ignored," thought Sitiyadai, reaching for the flowers and gently wove the white blossoms into her jet black hair. It soon looked like the night sky had descended on earth.

She heard her friends call out her name and looked up to see them waiting for her at the end of the lane. That evening, they were going to the neighbouring village for a festival. The girls half-danced all the way there and stayed through the night, till the very end.

As they returned home, chattering among themselves, Sitiyadai felt something tickle the back of her neck. She reached up and felt the velvety petals of the flowers. They were wilting and about to fall.

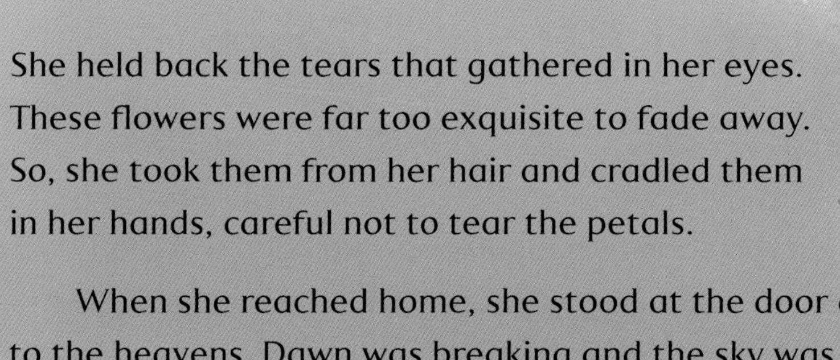

She held back the tears that gathered in her eyes. These flowers were far too exquisite to fade away. So, she took them from her hair and cradled them in her hands, careful not to tear the petals.

When she reached home, she stood at the door and looked up to the heavens. Dawn was breaking and the sky was turning golden. She smiled and whispered to the flowers in her hands, “You are far too pretty, far too precious, to fall on the ground.” So saying, she blew on them, her breath like a gentle breeze on a spring morning.

As if by magic, the petals fell away, transforming into butterflies. Some were big and some tinier than Sitiyadai’s little finger. Some were white as snow and others had black spots. Then, when the sun rose and its rays fell on the little creatures, their wings transformed into different hues of the rainbow.

The butterflies fluttered their wings and flew away in search of nectar.

The Helpful Chameleon

A Parsee oral tale

A tiny chameleon sat on the edge of a giant stone well and watched colourfully dressed soldiers marching through the sandy desert. He blinked as they stopped next to him. They had a hushed conversation and hid behind the well.

The sun blazed in the sky and the air shimmered in the heat. There were no trees or shrubs in the desert, just endless sand, dry and desolate. The chameleon, still perched on the well, blinked again as he saw a group of people in the distance, walking together. They were not really walking though, he could tell. They were shuffling and carrying their belongings in hastily tied bundles with children on their drooping shoulders. They looked tired with their clothes tattered and spirits spent.

These people were Zoroastrians, who lived in Persia but were now forced to leave their homes. An invasion by the Arabs had led to a bloody battle and the defeat of their king. The new rulers wanted the Zoroastrians to give up their beliefs and religion, and even destroyed their temples and scriptures. Terrified, they fled their homeland in search of a place where they could freely pray to their god and live in peace. Now as they made their journey across the desert, they were being chased by soldiers.

The chameleon blinked once again as the group picked up pace when they spotted the well and started walking towards it. They were hoping to quench their thirst with cool water. They did not know that soldiers with weapons were hiding behind the well.

Seeing them approach, the soldiers crouched a little more to hide the glint of their spears. The chameleon realized that the refugees were in danger and knew he had to do something. But how could he warn them?

Now, chameleons have a special ability. They can change their colour to match their surroundings. This skill protects them from many dangerous predators.

In a flash, the chameleon jumped on a soldier's turban, which was a deep maroon. His skin changed colour and became maroon. Then he jumped on the soldier wearing a blue turban. He paused for a minute and continued jumping down the line ...

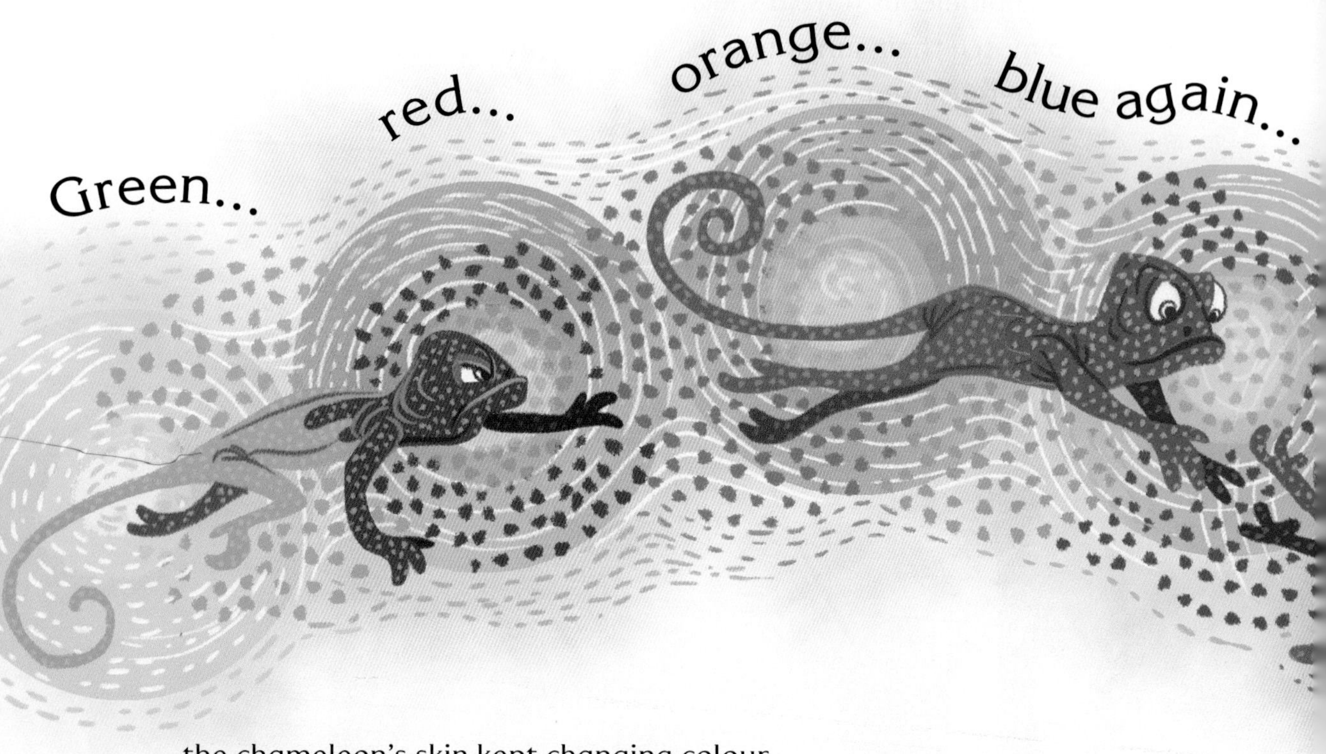

... the chameleon's skin kept changing colour.

From a distance, the weary travellers noticed a flash of colour in the otherwise bare desert. "*What was that?*" they wondered.

They stopped walking and peered at the well. After a quick discussion, they decided to send someone to investigate. The scout returned and told them of the soldiers hiding behind the well. He also informed them of the chameleon who was jumping on each turban, changing his appearance with every leap, and shaking his head, warning the scout from coming closer.

The group quickly changed their route to avoid the soldiers. As they left the path, they looked at the chameleon to thank him. The creature nodded his head, before jumping off the soldiers and blending into the sandy desert.

The Zoroastrians made it to the sea and then to India, where they came to be known as Parsees. Here, they could practise their religion in peace, and never forgot the chameleon who saved their lives.

Even today, centuries later, the Parsees treasure the chameleon or *sadda*. They call him *mama,* which means mother's brother.

Parsee children, to this day, look to their *sadda mama* when trying to make an important decision and wait to see if he will shake his head in a "no" or nod in a "yes".

Guest of the Blue Realm

A Khasi folk tale

Deep in a jungle in the Khasi hills lived U Klew, a peacock with brown feathers. Despite his ordinary appearance, U Klew thought he was royalty and had an ego to match. He had the highest tuft and a graceful train that was so long he could not enter the homes of smaller birds.

He spoke to only those he thought were the best of the best, and met them in courtyards large enough to fit his train.

Birds in neighbouring jungles sometimes even invited him as a chief guest to their festivals. All this made him think he was rather special and he became quite insufferable. He was rude to the smaller birds and was boastful too.

The other birds laughed behind U Klew's back but soon grew tired of his horrid behaviour. They decided to play a trick on him and hatched a plan. The next day, a parakeet and a blue jay flew to him with news. "U Klew, king of all the birds, you have been picked by the birds and animals in the jungle to meet Ka Sngi," the parakeet exclaimed.

Ka Sngi was the sun who lived in the Blue Realm, or heaven. She sent light, warmth, and sunshine to earth. Her smile brightened up everything around her.

U Klew's chest swelled with pride. "Of course, they would choose me."

The blue jay added in a mocking tone, "Who else but you can represent us birds? You are our king." The other birds watching nearby could not contain their laughter.

U Klew shook his tuft at this and said snobbishly, "I will fly up to the Blue Realm tomorrow and live there forever with the royal maiden. I am U Klew, the greatest of all the birds, and I deserve to live a life of heavenly luxury."

The next morning, the birds were surprised to see him preparing to fly up to the Blue Realm. They never thought that U Klew would go through with the plans. They had never seen him fly to a treetop. No one had seen him even take flight. Perhaps this prank had gone too far.

U Klew took a deep breath, flapped his wings, and rose up from the ground. His flight was a bit unsteady, but he went higher and higher. Soon, he was flying above the treetops. He kept flapping his wings until he reached the clouds. He looked back and his home seemed so tiny that it looked like speckled dust.

U Klew passed the earth and entered the realm of light and sunshine. Everything here was brighter and more beautiful than his home. He could see the entrance from a distance. Ecstatic, he flapped his wings as fast as he could and reached his destination.

In the Blue Realm, Ka Sngi got news of U Klew who had come from earth to stay with her. She had no friends as she had been forbidden to leave the Blue Realm and was happy to finally have company. But, U Klew was not who she expected.

Despite being in the most beautiful place in the universe, surrounded by light and everything he could possibly imagine, U Klew was still as mean, rude, and demanding as he was on earth. He would eat grapes only if they were fed to him. He wanted a golden chair that had his face engraved on it. He even wanted a room filled with mirrors so that he could see his reflection every day.

The kind maiden was happy to give him what he wanted, but U Klew's demands kept increasing. He took up so much of her time that she stopped shining her light on earth.

Back on earth, everyone was miserable. There was no sunshine. The birds stopped singing. Some days, U Slap, the torrid rain, washed away their cosy nests. There were other days when U Lyoh, the mist, invited dark clouds to cover the earth and did not allow any grain or fruit to grow. Sometimes, Ka Eriong, the storm, descended to destroy anything that came in her way. She shook the trees and ruined the ripened fruits and blooming flowers.

The birds realized that this was happening because of U Klew. He was taking up so much of Ka Sngi's time that she could no longer share her brightness with earth. They had to do something to bring him back.

They made their way to the home of Ka Sabuit, a crafty, old farmer, who lived in the same jungle. She had lost everything as well. Her crops were destroyed and the only thing she had left were a few mustard seeds. At first, she thought the birds were trying to steal from her. "Go away. I have nothing for you birds," she yelled from the window.

"Help us, Ka Sabuit," the birds pleaded.

She looked out and realized that the birds were weak and weary. They seemed too exhausted to do anything. She stepped out and heard their troubles. "That foolish peacock has ruined not just the Blue Realm but earth as well," she mumbled.

She thought for a minute and smiled. She knew how to bring U Klew back. She looked at the birds and said, "I will help you, but you must promise to protect my garden from pests and not eat my crops." The birds agreed and she got to work.

Ka Sabuit's field could be seen from the highest hills and even as far up as the Blue Realm. She planted the mustard seeds and the birds watched over her field and shooed away anyone who tried to eat the seeds. Then, she watered the field. They took such good care of the crop that her neighbours thought she was hiding gold and made fun of her.

Tiny, yellow mustard flowers bloomed but she continued watering and tending to the crop. Soon, she began re-shaping the field to look like a woman. In a short while, the field was in full bloom, and in the shape of a maiden. Everyone stopped to admire it.

Back in the Blue Realm, as U Klew continued his arrogant ways, Ka Sngi grew sadder by the day. He wanted to be pampered all the time. Ka Sngi, the excellent host, would fulfil his every wish, but U Klew wanted more. One day, the selfish peacock started thinking about earth. He had everything he ever wanted, but missed his home, friends, and all the fancy festivals he would attend. He wondered what the other birds were doing.

He hopped to the balcony and looked down to his old home. There, on earth, he saw a maiden dressed in gold. U Klew forgot all about Ka Sngi's generosity and decided to return at once. "I am leaving the Blue Realm. I must meet this mysterious golden maiden," he declared. He spread his wings and flew away.

Ka Sngi watched U Klew fly away and wept as her friend had abandoned her. Tears in the colours of the rainbow landed on the arrogant peacock's train. The Khasis call them *ummat ka sngi* or the sun's tears.

When U Klew reached his old home, the birds gathered around to admire his colourful new train. The peacock did not care. He wanted to see the golden maiden. "Where is she?" he demanded.

Giggling, the birds led him to Ka Sabuit's field. U Klew saw the mustard field in the shape of a maiden and figured out that he had been tricked. Desperate, for he realized he had made a mistake, U Klew flapped his wings to fly back to Ka Sngi and the Blue Realm. Try as he might, he could not fly again. He threw his head back and cried, hoping that Ka Sngi would hear him, but there was only silence.

In the Blue Realm, Ka Sngi cried for her friend, but soon felt a sense of great relief. She realized that she was free of the obnoxious U Klew. He no longer took up her time and she could once again light up every corner of the world below.

Back on earth, in the forest, U Klew became a changed bird. He grew sad and quiet. The other birds felt bad and they let him be.

He remained in the depths of the forest. He would only step out at the crack of dawn and fly as high as he could to the treetops. Then, he would open his beautiful train to greet Ka Sngi's morning sunlight, hoping that she could see him.

U Klew hoped that maybe,
one day, she would welcome him
back to the Blue Realm.

How to Trick a Tiger

A tale from the Suka Saptati

A princess and her two young sons were on their way to the Queen's palace. To get there, they had to cross a wide, dense jungle with great trees and fierce animals. After travelling the entire day, the princess decided to stop for the night. She found the perfect spot in a clearing in the jungle.

As the three settled down to eat, the princess heard a rustle. She looked up and, to her horror, spotted a ferocious tiger staring at her with bloodshot eyes. Crouched, he looked like he was ready to attack. The princess gulped, took a deep breath, and looked at her two children.

"Shhh. Stop arguing over who gets to eat this tiger," she pretended to scold them. "Eat this one first. We will look for another one after that."

The tiger could not believe his ears. He backed up a bit and looked at the woman. She had a glint in her eyes. He glanced at the two boys and thought they looked hungry.

With a piteous whimper, the tiger ran for his life. As he scrambled through the forest, he ran past a jackal, startling him.

The jackal had never seen a fierce tiger running in fear. “Hey tiger,” he called out. “Why are you running for your life? Have you seen a ghost? Or was it a demon?”

The terrified tiger stopped when he heard the jackal. “Run. Run,” he said in a trembling voice. “You should run too. There are three tiger-eating humans in this forest. I had only heard of them in stories, as a cub. Now, I have seen three!”

The jackal looked at the tiger and said, tilting his head, “That sounds like a lucky escape.”

“You have no idea,” the tiger said sobbing. “They were so close to me. They were ready to chop me into pieces and eat me!”

The jackal was curious. He had never seen tiger-eaters before. “I want to see one too,” he said.

“That is up to you. It makes no difference. Those humans are fierce. We are already doomed,” the tiger said, wailing. The jackal kept insisting until the trembling tiger agreed.

The jackal climbed onto the tiger's back, tying himself with a vine so that he would not fall off. Then, the two went to see the terrifying tiger-eaters.

The yellow-orange campfire burnt merrily in the clearing. The princess and her sons had settled down to eat when she heard a rustle. She looked up and, to her alarm, spotted the tiger once again. He now had a jackal on his back. What was she to do?

Before the two animals could come any closer, she called out, "Jackal! What are you doing? Why have you brought me one tiger? There was a time you would bring me three tigers to eat."

The tiger stopped and, with a pitiful cry, turned around and ran through the forest yet again. The confused jackal, still tied to his back, bounced about. The tiger did not care. He ran through the forest, swum across the river, scrambled over a mountain, and crossed through yet another forest. The jackal held on for his dear life. Finally, after what seemed like a long time, he burst out laughing. The tiger stopped when he heard the jackal.

"Why are you laughing? No one cracked a joke," he asked.

"It is quite funny if you think about it. We bested the tiger-eaters. I am safe because you helped us get out of danger," he said mockingly. "Could you please help me down now. I would like to see where we are."

The tiger helped the jackal get down and collapsed, exhausted. The jackal walked away, chuckling to himself. He couldn't wait to tell the other animals about the foolish tiger, who soon became a laughing stock across all the lands.

As a wise owl once said, "Those, like the tiger, who are strong but ignorant and unwise will always be fooled by others."

The Light of the Firefly

A story from the Katha Sarit Sagara

A long time ago, on a cold and dark night in a jungle, a group of monkeys walked together. They were searching for warmth and shelter. Suddenly, one of them spotted a faint yellow-green light bobbing in the distance.

"Look! Look!" she screeched pointing at the light. "Fire! Fire!"

"Fire? Fire? Where is the fire?" asked one of the monkeys, looking first left and then right. The others copied him, as they jumped up and down to stay warm, but could not spot the fire.

"See, see," the female monkey squealed and rushed towards the light. The other monkeys ran after her as well.

They reached a clearing in the forest and stared at the fire, their mouths wide open. It seemed to be floating in the air. The monkeys surrounded it, chattering to each other.

"Throw some grass on it," said one monkey.

"No, no, add some leaves," said another.

They threw grass and leaves on the floating fire and waited for it to burn. Nothing happened.

Then, one monkey fanned the fire and another one blew on it, hoping that it would become a bit bigger. Nothing happened.

A sparrow, on her way home, saw the monkeys and their strange behaviour. They had surrounded a little firefly who cast a yellow-green light across the forest floor. They were tearing grass and leaves and placing it on the firefly. One kept blowing at the little insect and another fanned it. The sparrow could not believe her eyes.

She called out, “Hey monkeys! What are you doing? Why are you bothering this firefly?

“Go away, silly sparrow,” the monkeys yelled. “We are building a fire. It is cold and we want to be warm.”

“Stop, stop,” shouted the sparrow. “That is a firefly. It is not fire. You are hurting it.”

“Go away!” shouted the monkeys.

“Stop, please stop,” cried the concerned sparrow as she flew around them. Irritated, a monkey picked up a pebble and threw it at her. Another monkey followed suit. Soon, all of them were throwing pebbles at the poor sparrow.

In the commotion, the firefly managed to escape. Even though it was out of danger, its light was dim for it did not want to be confused with fire again. Tired and dazed, it shook its wings, looked left and right to make sure there were no monkeys, and returned to the firefly colony. “Beware of monkeys,” it warned its friends, with a shudder.

As for the sparrow, she escaped the monkeys and perched on the nearest tree to catch her breath. A wise owl, who lived in that tree, had seen the whole thing.

"There are two lessons to learn," she hooted. "Always protect the defenceless and not all good advice is well received."

Dance of Seasons

A folk tale from Himachal Pradesh

Nestled amid mountains that seemed to scrape the sky was a sleepy little village. It was winter and life had come to a standstill, with little movement, festivities, or play. It was as if the entire village was hibernating.

Three brothers lived in this village with their families. One morning, before the sun was about to rise, the youngest brother woke up the eldest one. He had been up all night worrying. Icy winds and continuous snowstorms had made this winter harsh. "There is no wood for fire, water to drink, or food to eat. How will we survive?"

The eldest brother sighed, patted him, and said, "Do not fret. We will find a way to brave the cold. This stubborn storm has trapped us for far too long. We cannot allow it to keep us in our home anymore."

Determined to find food, the three brothers stepped out of their home carrying bows and arrows. A little red bird joined them on their journey, perching on the youngest one's shoulder. It would be their guide and lead them to their prey.

The snow on the path to the forest was deep and untouched, for no villager had dared to leave their home. The three brothers, hungry and desperate, trudged through it. The bird flew ahead as they passed weather-beaten houses consumed by the white tempest and colourful prayer flags that fluttered in the wind.

They crossed a monastery that clung to the mountain's side. The brothers halted there for a brief while to seek blessings from the head monk and prayed for the winter to pass. They continued on their journey, guided by the bird, as each whispered a prayer. "*Hum–Ho–Hum–Ho–Hum–Hum–Ho–Hum–Hum–Ho,*" they chanted while walking.

Suddenly, the bird chirped, the sound so clear that it cut through the wind. The brothers turned their heads and were amazed to see a blue sheep. It was beautiful, shining bright under the moonlight, with broad, curved horns and a spotless hide. "Look. We have seen one after a long time," exclaimed one of the brothers. "We must catch it."

The eldest brother took aim and shot an arrow at the blue sheep. He missed. "Quick," he cried. "Chase it." The red bird flew after it, chirping and guiding the brothers. The blue sheep leapt through the snow and disappeared into the silent, dense, grey forest.

The brothers chased it into the forest, vaulting over fallen logs like frogs in a pond, as crystals of ice and glittering snow fell around them. They reached a clearing and stopped. It seemed as though the blue sheep had been a figment of their imagination, fuelled by hunger and desperation.

Suddenly, they heard drumming, which echoed through the forest. Was it a ritual or maybe a sacrifice? The beats grew louder with each step they took. The youngest brother gulped and asked, "Where is it coming from?"

The red bird settled on the eldest brother's shoulder. He gestured to his siblings asking them to stay behind him, and walked towards the sound, an arrow strung on his bow, ready to strike. They hid behind a tree and watched, petrified.

Dhum–Dhum–Dhum.
Dhum–Dhuma–Dhum–Dhum ...

Figures danced around a fire that burnt bright despite the strong winds and almost blinding snow. They wore giant masks, bigger than their bodies, with slits for eyes. However, there were no eyes behind those masks, just inky darkness. Loose cloaks covered their bodies. One figure had a large drum hanging from the neck.

Dhum–Dhum–Dhum Dhum–Dhuma–Dhum Dhum...

The masked figures swayed and stomped with their sticks, dancing to the beats of the drum and the howling wind. As the brothers watched, they realized there was a pattern.

The masked figures first looked at the ground, pointing to it. They then raised their hands and called to the skies. They moved in circles around the fire, offering handfuls of snow to the sky as a sacrifice.

"I am scared," whispered the youngest brother.

"What are they? Where are they from? What if they harm us?" asked the second brother.

"Hush," admonished the eldest. "What if they hear us?"

Just then, the red bird flapped its wings vigorously, trying to catch their attention. One of the figures had heard them. It started running towards them and the eldest brother lifted his bow and shot it. He missed by an inch.

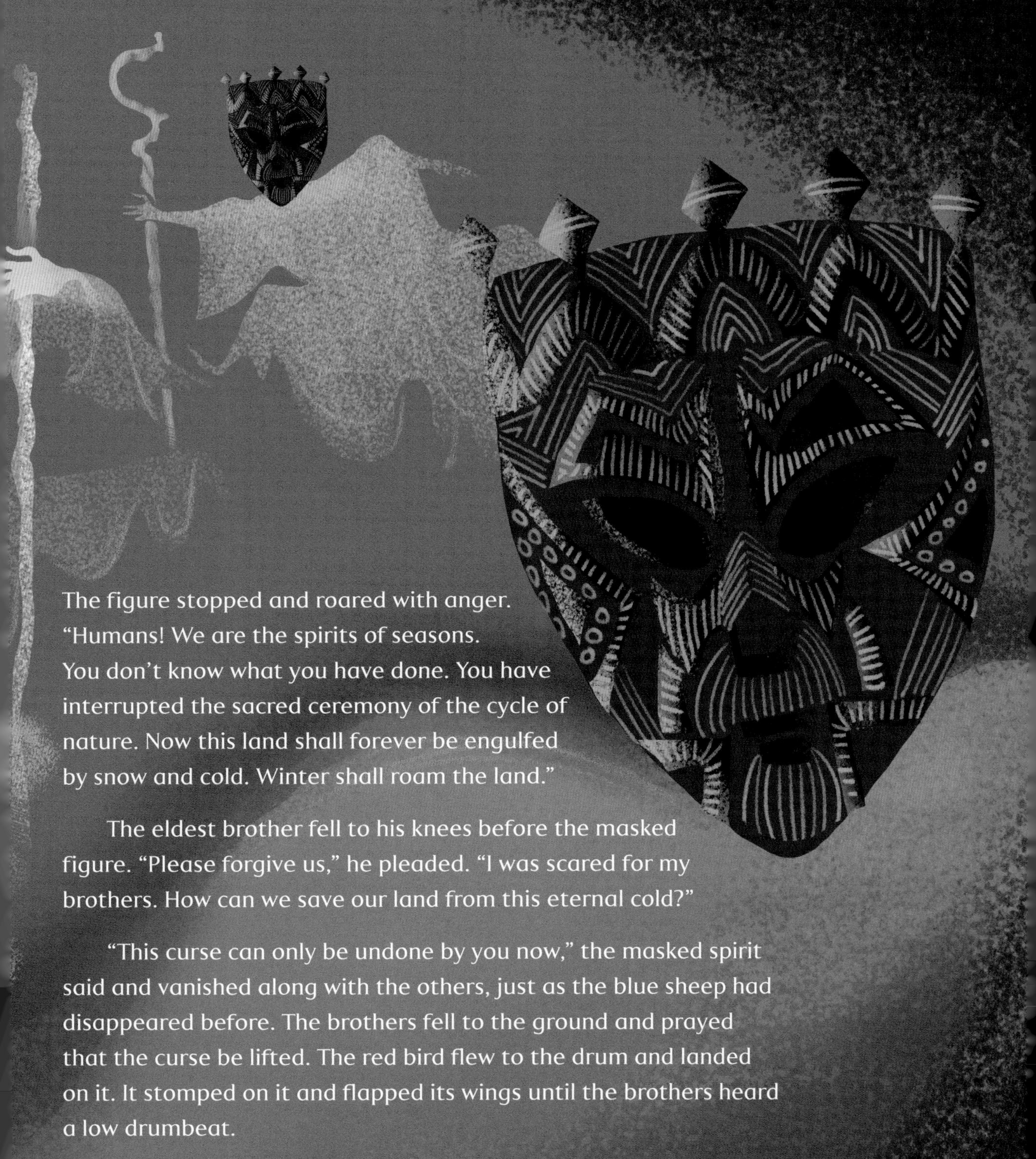

The figure stopped and roared with anger. "Humans! We are the spirits of seasons. You don't know what you have done. You have interrupted the sacred ceremony of the cycle of nature. Now this land shall forever be engulfed by snow and cold. Winter shall roam the land."

The eldest brother fell to his knees before the masked figure. "Please forgive us," he pleaded. "I was scared for my brothers. How can we save our land from this eternal cold?"

"This curse can only be undone by you now," the masked spirit said and vanished along with the others, just as the blue sheep had disappeared before. The brothers fell to the ground and prayed that the curse be lifted. The red bird flew to the drum and landed on it. It stomped on it and flapped its wings until the brothers heard a low drumbeat.

Dhum–Dhum–Dhum
Dhum–Dhuma–Dhum–Dhum …

The bird chirped at the brothers as if inviting them to join in. One brother picked up the drumsticks and started playing the drum. The other two moved to the beats, swaying and dancing around the fire, mimicking the steps of the masked spirits.

Dhum–Dhum–Dhum
Dhum–Dhuma–Dhum–Dhum …

They chanted and prayed, and soon found themselves in a deep trance, dancing to the drumbeats. They were determined to save their land and people from the eternal wrath of winter. The fire, which was the sun in its earthly form, glowed bright as ever. The bird danced too, flapping its wings.

Soon the fire glowed once more and a bright light shone through. The wheel of seasons turned once again. The blanket of snow melted, the land bloomed, and flowers dotted the forest floor.

The land shook off the winter and it was spring once again.

Even today, in the month of March, villagers in the Lahaul and Spiti valley come together for three days to celebrate the festival of Yor. They wear wooden masks and dance around an idol made of snow, praying for the wheel of seasons to turn, and for the coming of spring.

The Grain of Corn

A tale from Punjab

One summer morning, a farmer's wife was winnowing corn. It had been a great season and she was proud of the new crop as the corn was sweet and juicy.

A crow, flying past, saw the delicious, golden corn and his mouth began to water. He swooped down, snatched up a grain, and flew to a nearby tree.

The woman was fuming. In a fit of rage, she took a stick and flung it at the crow. Startled, the bird lost his balance and the grain of corn popped out of his beak and rolled into a crack at the foot of the tree.

The farmer's wife shook her fist at the crow and shouted, "Return my grain of corn or I will catch you and put you in a cage forever."

Petrified at the thought of living in a cage for the rest of his life, the crow tried to take out the grain of corn, which was now stuck in the crack. He clawed and pecked at it, but could not reach it. "I don't want to be caged," the crow cried. "I must save my life from the farmer's wife." So he flew to a woodcutter.

"Woodcutter! Woodcutter! Chop the tree.
As I cannot reach the grain of corn,
And I must save my life from the farmer's wife."

The woodcutter ignored him. So, the crow went to the palace to see the king.

"King! King! Jail the woodcutter.
The woodcutter won't chop the tree,
As I cannot reach the grain of corn,
And I must save my life from the farmer's wife."

The king had many royal matters to deal with and shooed away the crow. So, the bird went to the queen.

"Queen! Queen! Convince the king.
The king won't jail the woodcutter,
The woodcutter won't chop the tree,
As I cannot reach the grain of corn,
And I must save my life from the farmer's wife."

The queen was resting in her chamber and the chambermaids chased the crow away. So the crow left the palace and went to the garden. There he met a snake.

"Snake! Snake! Bite the queen.
The queen won't convince the king,
The king won't jail the woodcutter,
The woodcutter won't chop the tree,
As I cannot reach the grain of corn,
And I must save my life from the farmer's wife."

The snake stuck his tongue out at the crow and slithered away. The crow sighed and spotted a rope.

"Rope! Rope! Tie up the snake.
The snake won't bite the queen,
The queen won't convince the king,
The king won't jail the woodcutter,
The woodcutter won't chop the tree,
As I cannot reach the grain of corn,
And I must save my life from the farmer's wife."

But, the rope did not respond.
So, the crow looked for the mouse.

"Mouse! Mouse! Chew the rope.
The rope won't tie the snake,
The snake won't bite the queen,
The queen won't convince the king,
The king won't jail the woodcutter,
The woodcutter won't chop the tree,
As I cannot reach the grain of corn,
And I must save my life from the farmer's wife."

The mouse ignored the crow, so he
went to the cat.

"Cat! Cat! Chase the mouse,
The mouse won't chew the rope,
The rope won't tie up the snake,
The snake won't bite the queen,
The queen won't convince the king,
The king won't jail the woodcutter,
The woodcutter won't chop the tree,
As I cannot reach the grain of corn,
And I must save my life from the farmer's wife."

The cat's ears perked up when she heard of the mouse,
as she had been hunting for him for a while.

So the cat chased the mouse,
The mouse tried chewing the rope,
The rope started binding the snake,
The snake tried biting the queen,
The queen convinced the king,
The king decided to jail the woodcutter,
The woodcutter quickly chopped the tree.

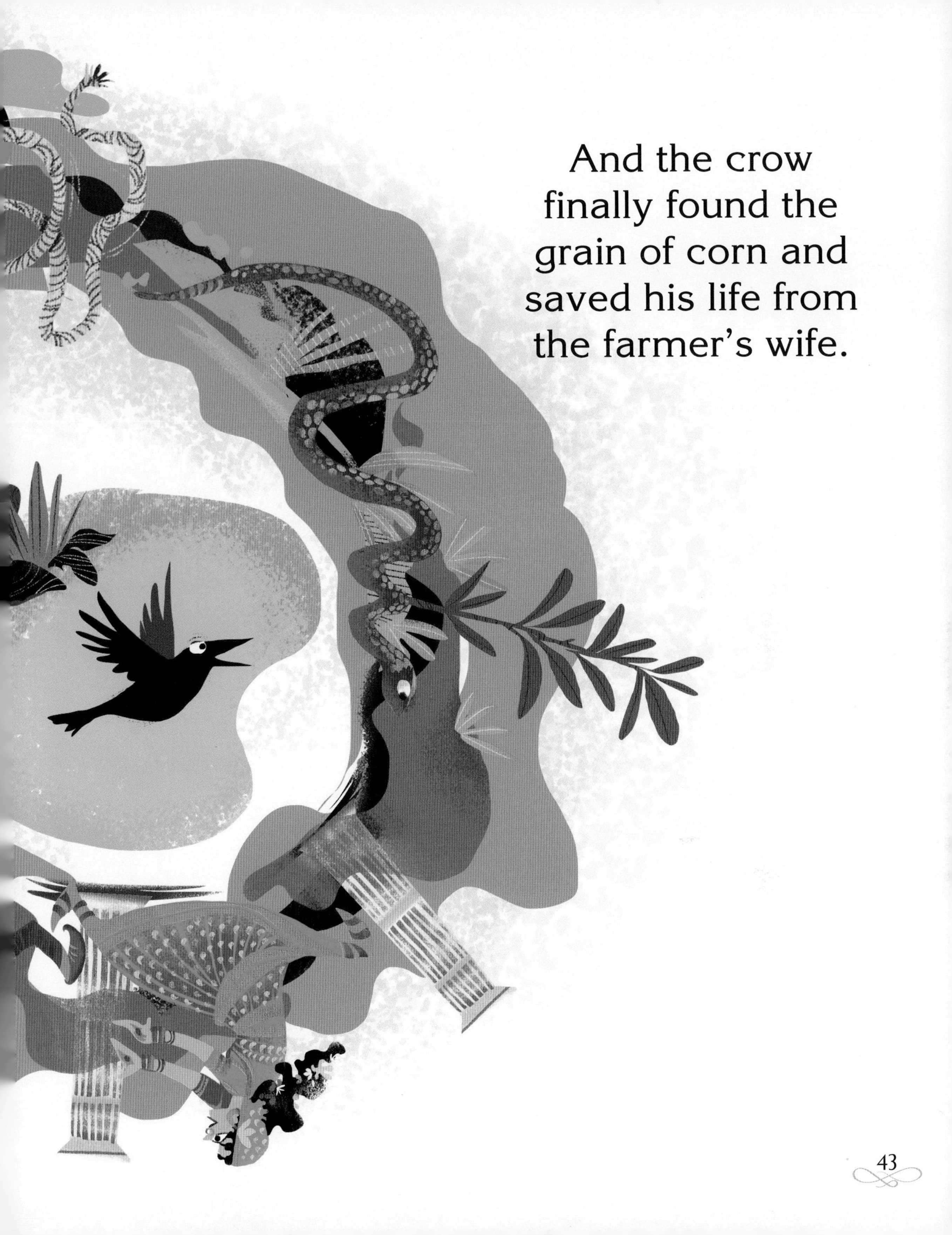

And the crow
finally found the
grain of corn and
saved his life from
the farmer's wife.

Revenge of the Snake

A tale from the Astika Parva in the Mahabharata

The mighty King Parikshit was worried. He had just seven days to live and he did not know what to do. He locked himself inside the tallest tower in his palace in Hastinapura, the capital of the powerful kingdom of Kuru. He did not eat or sleep, and instead paced the length of his lonely tower. Soon, he turned pale, like the moon on a very cloudy day, and as restless as the wind.

When the citizens of Hastinapura heard that their king had barricaded himself in a tower, they whispered, "Our king's forefathers were the god-like Pandavas, his father was the valorous Abhimanyu, and yet he cowers in his tower."

King Parikshit soon told his trusted advisors the truth. He had been cursed. He recounted how he lost his way while chasing a stag on a hunting trip.

He walked for hours on wild paths and around ancient trees, which touched the sky. Then, amid an orchestra of birdsongs, he saw a *rishi*, or a sage, meditating outside his hut.

The king approached the sage and demanded to know where the stag had disappeared. Sages, when they meditate, can be lost in worlds beyond our own. So Sage Shamika did not hear the king's voice. Angry at being ignored, the king wrapped a dead snake around his neck. It was a grave mistake.

The sage's young son, Sringin, had a temper. When he heard about Parikshit's behaviour, he cursed the king. "You, foolish king, will die in the next seven days. You used a snake to disrespect my father, and it will be a snake that will kill you," he shouted.

Of course, when the calm Sage Shamika emerged from his meditation, he was not pleased. "Anger is never the way, especially for sages. We are peaceful beings and are supposed to protect humanity. There was no need to be rash," he told his son. The damage, however, had been done.

Scared of the curse, Parikshit now locked himself in the tower. The windows and doors were sealed so that even ants could not crawl in. Everyone entering the palace was checked. He even issued bounties to kill snakes and called for court mystics to perform protection charms.

Takshaka, a *naga*, had decided to fulfil the curse. The *nagas* were ancient serpent-humans, who lived in *patala lok*, the netherworld. Their palaces were grand, green, and lit with the brilliance of a billion jade stones. All sorts of *nagas* lived there – winged cobras, purple pythons, fiery kraits, and some who looked like humans, but had forked tongues.

Takshaka had magical powers. He could shrink or expand, either becoming as big as a dragon or as small as a worm. He was determined to kill the king and made it his life's mission.

He transformed into a worm and burrowed his way into a bright red apple. On the evening of the seventh day, as fate would have it, this apple made its way to the king's tower. When the king picked up the fruit, he noticed a wormhole and before he could throw it, a tiny worm popped out. It grew to become a giant snake with luminous scales.

Hissing, Takshaka leapt at Parikshit and coiled himself around the king's neck, suffocating him till he could not breathe. Then, he bit him.

Death, as inevitable as day turning to night, came for King Parikshit. When the guards found him, he was dead and his killer was nowhere to be found.

Takshaka had turned into a worm, too small to be seen, and slithered away into the silence.

How to Fool an Alligator

A tale from Southern India

A hungry jackal left his den in the side of a hill and walked to the river looking for some juicy crabs. He had avoided the river for a long time, for it was the home of a vicious alligator with razor-sharp teeth. Now he was too hungry to care.

He made his way to the edge of the river and saw a scared crab scuttling away. Ecstatic, he dove to catch it. Little did he know that the alligator was hiding among the bulrushes, pretending to be asleep. He caught the jackal's foot with a swoop even as the crab fled to safety.

At first, the jackal panicked. *Oh no! What do I do? This alligator will eat me.* He took a few deep breaths and calmed down when he realized that the only way to escape was if he fooled the beast. "You are so smart," teased the jackal trying to keep his voice calm. "You have caught the bulrush, not my paw. Isn't it so soft?"

The startled alligator thought for a moment. There was no panic in the jackal's voice and the bulrushes blocked his view. *Maybe he is telling the truth,* the alligator thought and released his grip.

The jackal jumped away, chuckling loudly, and yelled, "You let me go." The alligator was furious and promised himself that he would eat the wily creature next time.

The jackal returned to the river the next day to try again. He kept a lookout for the alligator who he knew was hiding somewhere along the river's edge. "Every time I hunt for crabs, I look for the ones that peep through the mud," he said in a loud voice. "I can't see any now."

The alligator, hidden under the mud, thought that he could fool him. He poked his snout out a little so that the jackal would think it is a crab, but in doing so, gave away his hiding place.

"There you are, alligator. I see you. Don't worry I will hunt somewhere else," the jackal shouted and scampered off. Irritated, the alligator promised to take revenge.

The next day, he stayed close to the river's edge and waited. The jackal walked up and could not spot his nemesis. So he shouted, "I wonder where all the crabs are? If they are underwater, I can usually see them go *bubble, bubble, bubble*. And then the bubbles go *pop, pop, pop*."

This is my moment. I am going to fool the jackal, catch him, and eat him, thought the alligator. The giant beast took a deep breath, slipped underwater, and blew bubbles with his very large snout.

Puff, puff, puff, he blew. The water went *bubble, bubble, bubble*. These were not delicate bubbles, but giant ones, which went *pop, pop, pop* quite loudly, giving away the alligator's hiding place.

"There you are, alligator," shouted the jackal. "Thank you for showing me where you are." So saying, he ran back to his den in the hill, resolving never to return. There had been far too many narrow escapes.

The alligator grumbled and waited for the jackal to return. Days passed, but he did not see the wily creature. The jackal, you see, had decided to eat figs instead of risking his life. He found his new meal very light, but filling, and best of all, they fell from a tree on their own.

When the alligator heard about this, he decided to go after him. *This time he will not get away*, he thought, and crawled all the way to the hill. There he saw the fig tree and buried himself under the leaves and fallen fruit. He snacked on them while he waited.

The jackal, of course, had heard the birds and animals talk about the massive creature who had crawled all the way from the river to the hill. An alligator strolling about made for a funny sight, after all. So, he was quite prepared.

He walked up to the fig tree and called out, "I love juicy, ripe figs. They tumble down the tree and roll wherever the breeze takes them. Those are the best figs." He paused and then said, "This giant heap of figs does not look right. They can't be ripe. I will not eat them."

The alligator shook himself and the pile, but he was not gentle like a breeze. Instead, the leaves scattered and tiny figs rolled everywhere leaving the alligator quite exposed and visible.

"Thank you alligator, you have helped me find you. I should have known it was you hiding beneath the leaves and figs," teased the jackal and left.

The embarrassed alligator was furious as he had never been tricked so many times. He followed the jackal and found his den. He sat outside the next day, until the jackal had left, then crept in and waited for him to return. *How would the jackal escape now?*

The jackal returned and realized something was not right. The smudged ground looked as if something heavy had crawled in. Could this be his old nemesis? He had to be sure.

"Hello my lovely home," he called out. He waited a moment and then said, "Why don't you answer? Is something wrong? You always reply."

The alligator waiting inside did not know what to do and decided to answer. "Hello, hello, everything is fine. Come on in."

Hearing the alligator's voice, the jackal dropped all his figs and raced to the other side of the river to start over. The alligator tried to keep up, but the jackal was too fast.

Tired, the alligator gave up and returned to the river. He did develop a taste for figs, however. So when he couldn't catch crabs, fish, or smart jackals, he ate figs instead.

The First Eclipse

A Khasi folk tale

In a time when the world was far younger than it is now, there was a little girl named Ka Nam. She lived in a small village at the edge of a forest, near undulating hills and rolling meadows.

With eyes that sparkled, long black hair that grazed her ankles, a kind heart, and unparalleled grace, she was the loveliest in all the lands. Her mother often worried that someone would kidnap her and told her to stay away from the forest.

One day, the mother's worst fears came true when U Khla, a big and ferocious tiger, saw Ka Nam near a spring where she was filling a water pitcher. In a flash, he grabbed the little girl and took her to his den, deep in the forest.

Ka Nam was afraid at first and then surprised when she saw that U Khla was as gentle and affectionate as her parents. He offered her everything – nice clothes, tasty food, and even books from the village. What Ka Nam did not know was that U Khla was waiting for her to grow up, so that he could eat her.

Years passed until one day U Khla felt she was big enough and would make a good meal. He told her, "My Ka Nam, tonight, we will host a feast. My friends from the forest will be here. You must make sure that the den is clean and ready." Ka Nam did not suspect a thing and busied herself making the den ready for the guests.

A little mouse with big ears and long whiskers knew of U Khla's plan and whispered into Ka Nam's ear, "You are in grave danger. I heard U Khla talking to his friends today. He was only nice and brought you delicious food so that, one day, he could fatten you up and eat you. Today is that day."

Shocked and scared, Ka Nam started crying. How would she escape? The den was too deep in the mountain and the path outside, confusing. If she did manage to escape, wouldn't U Khla come after her? He was so powerful, after all.

The mouse, however, had a plan. She took Ka Nam to the one creature in the entire forest who could help her escape, the giant toad, U Hynroh.

The entire forest feared the malevolent U Hynroh. The giant toad with beady eyes and a slimy, green body had magical powers. He agreed to help but asked for a horrifying promise in exchange.

Ka Nam could never leave U Hynroh and had to wear an ugly toadskin all the time. "If you run away or take the skin off," he told her in an oily voice that made her shudder, "you will pay a terrible price."

The mouse saw the lovely maiden in the hideous toadskin and realized that she would be U Hynroh's slave forever. There was only one thing left to do.

The mouse took her to the magic tree in the heart of the forest. This was the entrance to the Blue Realm, where the moon, stars, and Ka Sngi, the sun, lived. Perhaps Ka Nam would be safe there, she hoped. The maiden climbed the tree and chanted the words the mouse had taught her:

"*Oh dear tree, grow tall and expand for the sky is near.*
Oh dear tree, grow tall and expand for the sky is dear!"

The tree grew taller and taller, until it grazed the sky. Ka Nam climbed up the tree and into the Blue Realm, far, far away from the tiger and the toad.

She wandered through the Blue Realm looking for a place to stay. She was turned away from every home, because she still wore the ugly toadskin, which she was too scared to remove. Sad and tired, Ka Nam reached the dazzling palace of Ka Sngi and begged her for a place to stay.

Ka Sngi, taking pity on this strange, toad-like girl, let her stay in a small room close to her palace. Living under the sun's care, Ka Nam soon felt safe. One day, feeling a little less scared, she took off the hideous toadskin before going to a spring for a bath. Ka Sngi happened to see the skin and realized that the girl was under an evil spell. She burnt the toadskin to ashes. Ka Nam was now free.

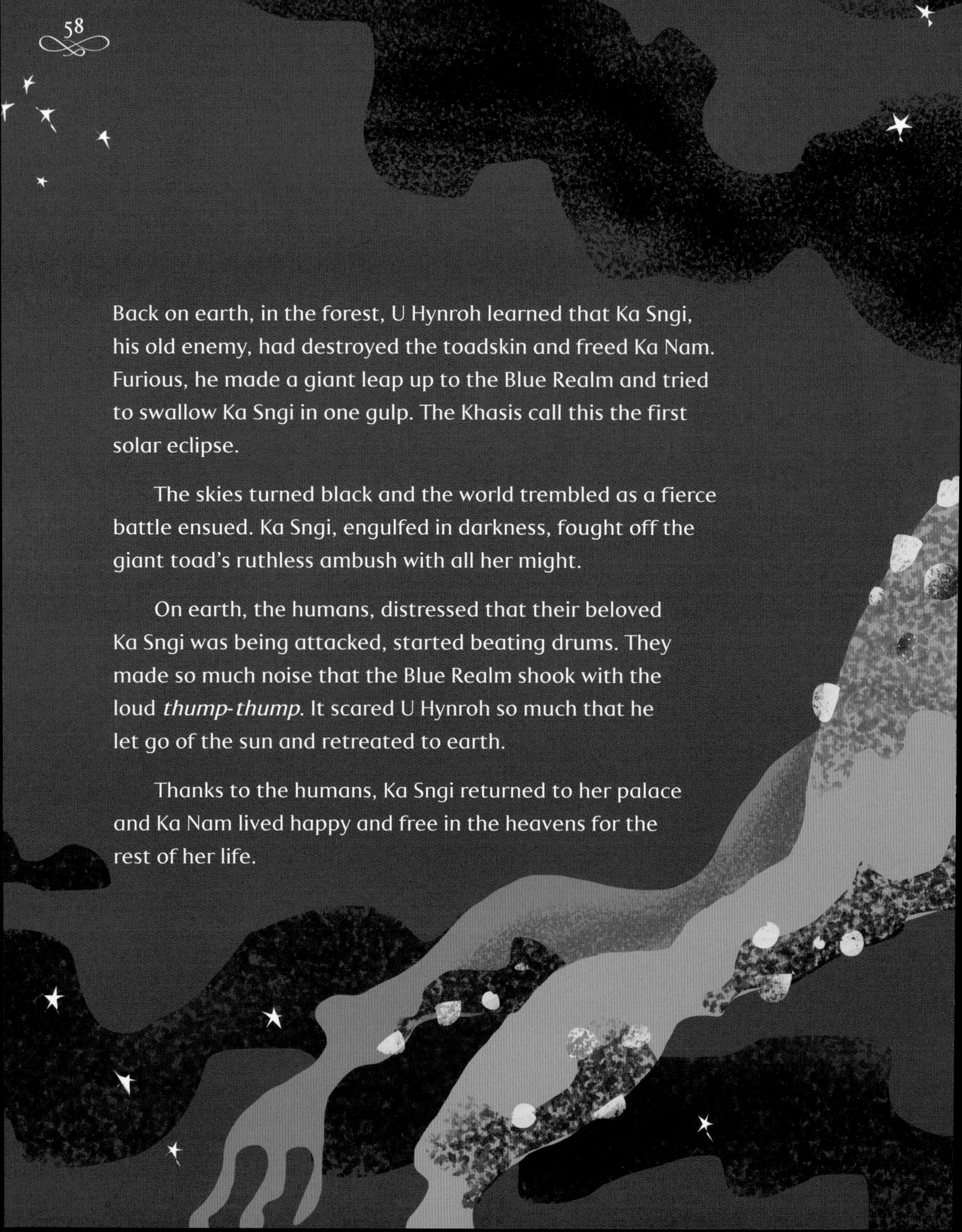

Back on earth, in the forest, U Hynroh learned that Ka Sngi, his old enemy, had destroyed the toadskin and freed Ka Nam. Furious, he made a giant leap up to the Blue Realm and tried to swallow Ka Sngi in one gulp. The Khasis call this the first solar eclipse.

The skies turned black and the world trembled as a fierce battle ensued. Ka Sngi, engulfed in darkness, fought off the giant toad's ruthless ambush with all her might.

On earth, the humans, distressed that their beloved Ka Sngi was being attacked, started beating drums. They made so much noise that the Blue Realm shook with the loud *thump-thump*. It scared U Hynroh so much that he let go of the sun and retreated to earth.

Thanks to the humans, Ka Sngi returned to her palace and Ka Nam lived happy and free in the heavens for the rest of her life.

Now and then, even today,
the giant toad tries to
engulf Ka Sngi and causes
a solar eclipse. When that happens,
the Khasis beat their drums
and scare him away.

The Matchmaker and the Leopard

A Santali folk tale

A very long time ago, when there were no cities, just a handful of villages and an almost never-ending forest, there lived a matchmaker. Every day, he would cut through the forest to visit families and arrange marriages. Along the way, he was careful not to bump into wild animals, especially leopards on the prowl.

Little did he know that a female leopard had heard of him. Intrigued, she waited for the day she would bump into him because she had resolved to eat him.

One morning, as always, the matchmaker took his usual route through the woods. He was cautious and made sure he stuck to the path. As he walked, his stomach growled. It was too dangerous to stop, but he was hungry. He took out his lunch from the sack he was carrying and sat down for a quick meal. Once the matchmaker finished, he flung the empty sack around his shoulders and stood up to continue his journey and shrieked.

Right in front of him stood a female leopard with beautiful black spots on her golden fur. She stared at him, unblinking.

The matchmaker gulped. "Please do not eat me, leopard. I have a really important job to do. If I die then who will do my job?"

The leopard's ears turned up. "What important job?" she asked.

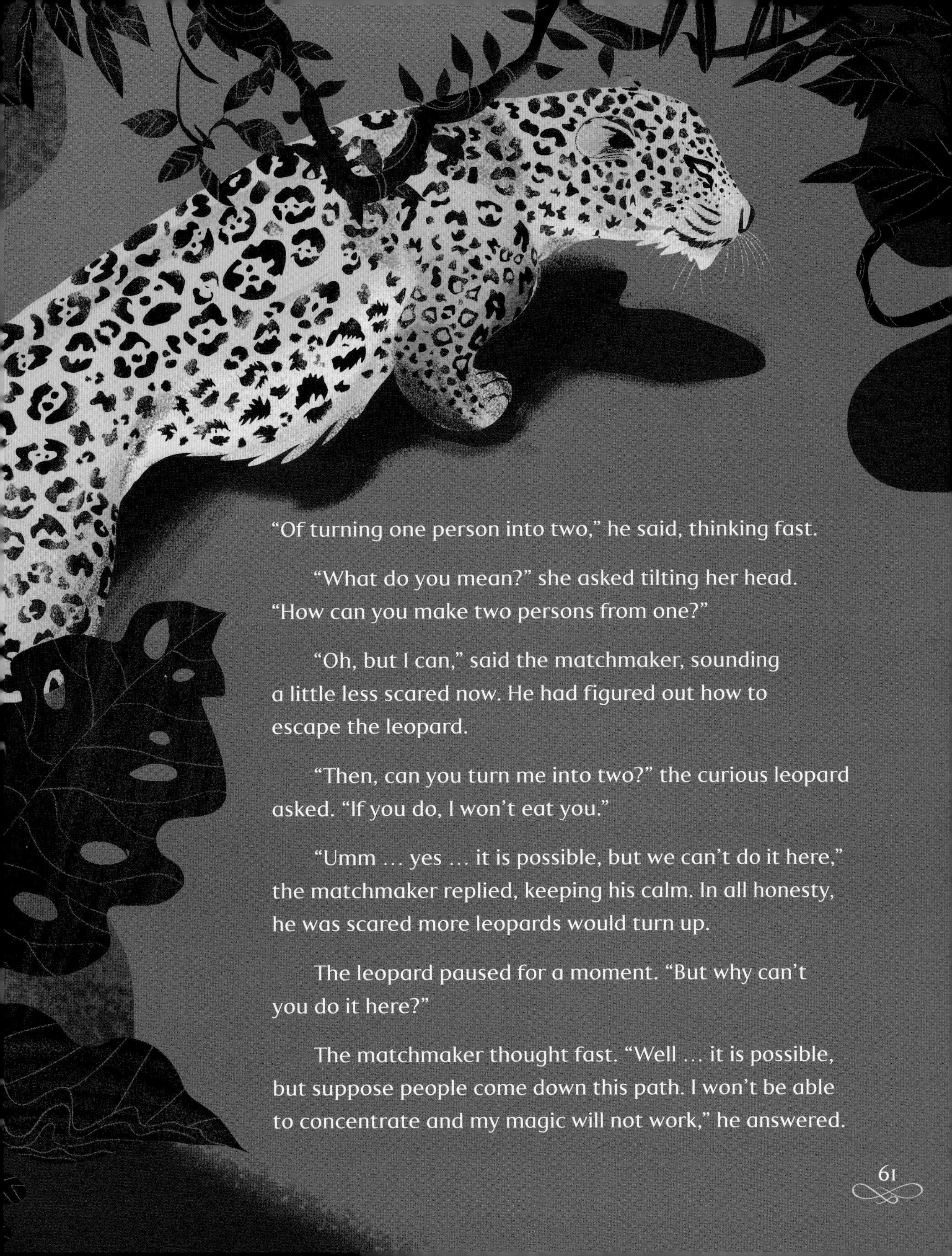

"Of turning one person into two," he said, thinking fast.

"What do you mean?" she asked tilting her head. "How can you make two persons from one?"

"Oh, but I can," said the matchmaker, sounding a little less scared now. He had figured out how to escape the leopard.

"Then, can you turn me into two?" the curious leopard asked. "If you do, I won't eat you."

"Umm … yes … it is possible, but we can't do it here," the matchmaker replied, keeping his calm. In all honesty, he was scared more leopards would turn up.

The leopard paused for a moment. "But why can't you do it here?"

The matchmaker thought fast. "Well … it is possible, but suppose people come down this path. I won't be able to concentrate and my magic will not work," he answered.

The leopard nodded, believing him. The relieved matchmaker opened up the empty sack. "Hop into this sack and I will carry you to a spot where I can chant my mantra," he said. As the leopard sat inside the sack, the matchmaker said, "Now you must be quiet. My magical powers will not work if it is noisy and you won't become two."

He tied the sack tightly so that the leopard would not escape and walked towards the river. There, he flung the sack into the water and ran home, promising himself that he would never stop while walking through the forest.

Meanwhile, the sack floated down the river. The leopard, curled up inside, tried to not make a sound. She squeezed her eyes shut and waited.

At the bottom of the river, a male leopard was drinking water. He spotted the massive sack floating towards him. "Is that a cow?" he asked the birds flying above him. *It must be a cow,* he thought. The sack floated by and the leopard grabbed it with his teeth and pulled it ashore. He used his claws and teeth to untie it.

Out popped the female leopard who blinked and then declared happily, "The matchmaker's magic worked. I have become two."

The male leopard was confused, but happy to gain a companion. He listened to the female leopard's encounter with the matchmaker with fascination.

Then the two decided to never eat matchmakers and they lived together happily ever after.

Sir Talk-a-Lot

A story from East India

There once lived a king who talked too much. His name was Bahadur and he was known to say the silliest things. His minister, Hazar, constantly worried for the people of the kingdom thought their king was a joke. When the king's royal chariot would go by, they would say, "Beware, Sir Talk-a-Lot is here." Something had to be done. But, what?

In the king's garden lived a turtle who had the same problem. He was worse than Bahadur and had caused many fights in the pond. Everyone disliked him and no one spoke to him. Tired of the situation, the turtle decided he wanted a fresh start.

It so happened that, around this time, the king had moved to his summer palace and was waiting for Hazar to join him. Before the journey, Hazar took a stroll in the garden and overhead the strangest conversation.

The turtle was talking to two ducks who were preparing to leave the pond. "Hey! Ducks. Look here. Where are you going?" the turtle asked.

"We are flying to a golden cave near the summer palace," they replied.

"I want to go too. I want my own pond. I don't want to live here anymore," he said. This was his chance to leave and the ducks were happy to take him. They grabbed a stick with their beaks and asked him to hold on to it with his mouth. The ducks warned, "Don't talk, or you'll fall."

The talkative turtle reminded Hazar of the king. He was sure that the creature would not survive the journey. Shaking his head, he left for the summer palace.

The ducks flew over villages and fields. The loudmouth turtle mumbled throughout the journey: "Look at those people ... look at the huts ... look at the sky."

"Don't talk, or you'll fall," the ducks warned him again and again.

As they reached the palace, a lady, pointed at them, for they were quite a sight, and yelled, "Look, a turtle flying with ducks."

The turtle could not stop himself. He huffed, looked down, and shouted back, "What is it to you! Mind your own business." As he did so, he let go of the stick and fell from the sky.

That was the end of the talkative turtle, who plunged to his death in the courtyard of the summer palace, where Bahadur and Hazar were walking. The king was shocked and when Hazar told him the turtle's story, he fell silent. He realized the importance of thinking before speaking, or he too would be doomed.

Over time, King Bahadur became wise, discreet, and measured and soon the people of his kingdom began to respect and love him.

Garuda, the King of Birds

A tale from the Astika Parva in the Mahabharata

Rishi Kashyapa, father to the *asuras*, the *devas*, and all of earth's living creatures, married the daughters of Daksha, one of the creators of the universe. One day, he decided to grant a boon to each of his beloved wives, Kadru and Vinata.

"I wish to be the mother of a thousand snakes! Let them all be equally strong and splendid," announced Kadru, leaping with excitement.

"And you, Vinata?" enquired Kashyapa.

"I wish to have two sons, superior to all the sons of Kadru. Let them be stronger, more energetic, and all-powerful," replied Vinata.

"It shall be so," Kashyapa told his wives. "You shall each bring forth eggs, from which your children will be born." Then, he walked away into the forest to meditate.

After a long period of waiting, Kadru's thousand eggs hatched, and out sprung her serpentine sons. Watching her sister, Vinata grew jealous and impatient. *Why have my sons not hatched? Perhaps they need some help*, she wondered.

She picked up one of the eggs and cracked it open gently. Inside lay her half-formed son who opened his eyes and looked at her in anger. "Your impatience will cost you. You will be bound by servitude. You will have to wait patiently for 500 years for the other egg to hatch. Only my brother can free you from slavery," he cursed her in a booming voice. Then, he flew towards the heavens, where he became known as Aruna, the sun god's charioteer.

His words came true. Years went by and Vinata, upon losing a wager one day, was tricked into slavery by Kadru. She served her sister and her thousand snake children for 500 years, until one day, the second egg cracked open.

A mighty, resplendent eagle burst forth. Garuda, the king of all birds, shone fiercer than the flames of the sacred fire, and his eyes flashed brighter than lightning. He spread his wings and grew in size, covering the earth and reaching the heavens. When he opened his beak to speak, the ground quaked. The gods trembled at the sight, but knew he had been born to protect his mother and the world. They requested him to show mercy on the earth and the heavens, so he made himself smaller.

Garuda watched his mother serve Kadru and her sons and asked, "Mother, why do you always see to their whims? Why must these vile snakes always lord over you?"

"This is my misfortune, my son. They deceived me one fateful day, and have forced me to serve them," his mother replied.

Angry, Garuda went to the snakes, "Tell me, what will it take to buy my mother's freedom?"

"We desire *amrit*, the divine nectar of immortality. Bring it to us and we will let your mother go," they said. Without losing a moment, Garuda grew in size, becoming bigger than the trees and the mountains. He spread his wings and flew towards the heavens.

As he approached the land of the *devas*, there were terrible omens. Thunderbolts blazed across the heavens and flaming meteors shot down from the sky.

Alarmed the *devas* prepared for battle, terrified yet determined to protect the *amrit* at any cost. They donned their gold-plated armour and drew out their deadliest weapons, the magical swords, maces, discuses, tridents, and axes. They placed the *amrit* in the centre of a giant, sharp-edged, revolving discus, guarded by a pair of hideous, poisonous serpents. A brilliant wall of fire surrounded the discus and the armed *devas* stood by it, waiting for Garuda to arrive.

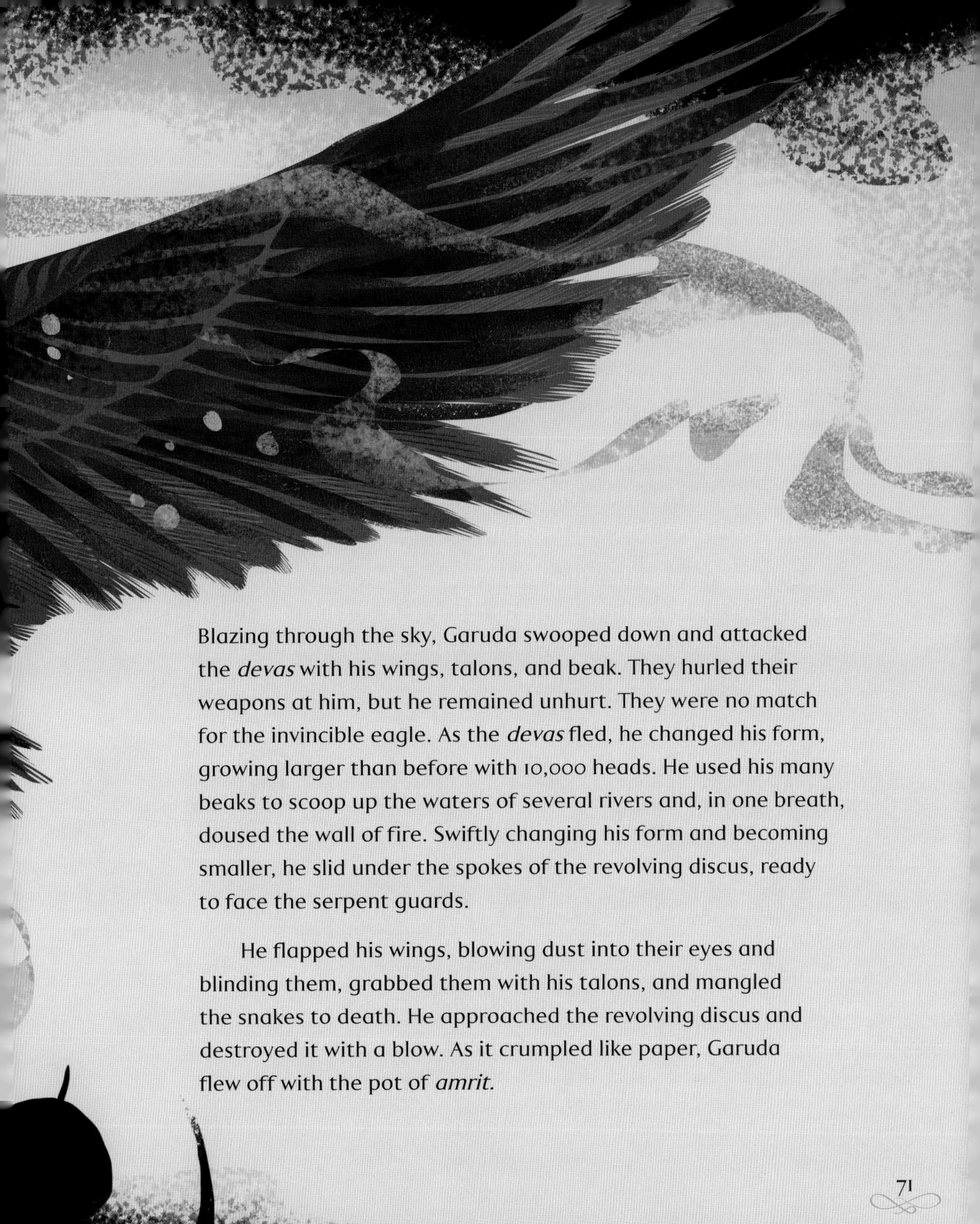

Blazing through the sky, Garuda swooped down and attacked the *devas* with his wings, talons, and beak. They hurled their weapons at him, but he remained unhurt. They were no match for the invincible eagle. As the *devas* fled, he changed his form, growing larger than before with 10,000 heads. He used his many beaks to scoop up the waters of several rivers and, in one breath, doused the wall of fire. Swiftly changing his form and becoming smaller, he slid under the spokes of the revolving discus, ready to face the serpent guards.

He flapped his wings, blowing dust into their eyes and blinding them, grabbed them with his talons, and mangled the snakes to death. He approached the revolving discus and destroyed it with a blow. As it crumpled like paper, Garuda flew off with the pot of *amrit*.

On his way back, Garuda met Vishnu, the preserver of the universe, who was pleased that the majestic bird had not tasted a single drop of the *amrit*. "I am impressed by your ability to resist temptation, Son of Vinata," he said. "I grant you the boon of immortality." Garuda bowed his head in gratitude and offered Vishnu a boon as well. "Be my mount, henceforth," requested Vishnu. Garuda agreed, promising to return once he had completed his task.

Then, Indra, the king of gods, approached Garuda, amazed at his strength and magnificence. "Mighty Garuda," he called out, "I offer you my lifelong friendship. Ask me for any boon that you desire."

Reflecting on his snake brothers' mistreatment of his mother, Garuda replied, "I wish for snakes to become my food."

Indra agreed and then made a request. "Take the *amrit* to your brothers, but we must find a way to retrieve it. It must not fall into the hands of those who do not deserve it." Garuda agreed and they devised a plan to protect the potion from the snakes.

When Garuda arrived home bearing the *amrit*, he offered it to his brothers and said, "I will place this pot on the grass. Go and bathe in the holy river, perform your sacred rites, and then you may drink to your heart's content. I have fulfilled your demand. Now you must free my mother."

The snakes nodded and before slipping away to the holy river said, "We grant your mother her freedom." No sooner had they left that Indra flew in, scooped up the pot of *amrit*, and disappeared. The snakes returned from their bath and found it gone. They licked the grass furiously, hoping to taste a few drops of *amrit* that may have fallen.

Alas, the *amrit* was gone, but the sharp-bladed grass sliced their tongues in two. Since that day, snakes have had forked tongues.

In the end, justice was served. Garuda freed his mother and whenever he was hungry, he feasted merrily on snakes.

The Tricksy Monkey

A story from Southern India

Deep in a jungle, a monkey sat on a tree, gobbling wood-apples. As he swung to another branch to eat more fruit, he felt a sharp stab of pain. A long, pointy thorn was stuck deep in his tail.

Hurt, but still eating wood-apples, the monkey climbed down the tree and walked to a village in search of help. He stopped when he spotted a barber in his shop. "Mister Barber," he called out. "Please help me. Remove this thorn."

The barber took pity on the poor monkey and pulled out his favourite razor. As he got to work, he accidentally snipped off the tip of the monkey's tail.

"Ah!" wailed the monkey. "Give back my tail. If you don't, you will have to give me your razor." There was no way that the barber could give the monkey his tail back. He had no choice, but to hand over his razor. The monkey grabbed it and ran off into the jungle, quite pleased with himself. He had also forgotten all about the thorn and his snipped tail.

In the jungle, he spotted a carpenter struggling to cut timber from a dried up tree. "Madame Carpenter," the monkey yelled. "Use my sharp razor. It will help you chop the tree." The grateful carpenter thanked the monkey and started cutting the timber. Soon, the razor turned blunt and broke.

"Oh no!" exclaimed the monkey looking at the razor, which was now quite useless. "What have you done? I want a new razor. If you can't give me one, then give me the timber." Now, how was the carpenter supposed to get a new razor? She was in the middle of a jungle. She had no choice but to give the monkey the timber she had cut with such difficulty.

The crafty monkey decided to sell the timber and walked towards the market. While strolling down the street, he saw a baker selling sweet *appams* and started feeling hungry.

"Madame Baker, it looks like you have run out of fuel. Why don't you use this timber and maybe make me some *appams* as well?"

Taken aback by his kindness, the baker thanked him, accepted the timber. She started making more *appams* and gave the monkey some to eat as well. Soon, the timber turned to ash and the baker ran out of fuel.

"What have you done, Baker! You have destroyed my timber. I want it back, or else give me all the *appams*," screamed the obnoxious monkey.

The baker had no other choice, but to give him all the *appams*. She was distraught. She had worked so hard and had nothing to show for it.

Meanwhile, the dreadful monkey strutted down the street carrying a stack of *appams*. He spotted a musician playing a drum and asked, "Would you like some *appams*, Mister Musician?"

It was almost dinnertime and the musician was hungry. Grateful, he took the *appams* and ate them all.

"My *appams*! My *appams*!" shrieked the sly monkey. "You have eaten all of them. Give them back or give me your drum." The musician had no choice but to give it to the monkey.

Satisfied, the monkey hopped and skipped to the jungle.

Dhum, Dhum, Dhum. He beat the drum. *Dhum, Dhum, Dhum.*

"*First, I lost my tail and gained a razor*," he sang.

The birds, animals, and humans stayed away from him. They had been hearing stories of the tricksy monkey all day.

Dhum, Dhum, Dhum, he beat the drum. "*Then, I lost my razor and gained a lot of timber*," he sang.

"I lost my timber and got so many delicious appams."

"And then, I lost my appams, but got this drum and drumsticks!" Dhum, Dhum, Dhum.

He sang the song again and again, rather shamelessly.

The animals could not believe that the nasty monkey had not been punished for the horrible things he had done. They went to the wise, old owl to complain.

She sighed and said: "There are many in this world who exploit others for no reason. Don't worry, this monkey's trickery will not last. For those who lie and cheat, end up with no friends."

Sure enough, everyone ignored the mean monkey and hid from him when they heard his silly song. He may have gained a drum to play with, but the monkey soon found himself quite alone.

Journey Across the Ocean

A tale from the Janamsakhis

Guru Nanak and his companions, Bhai Bala and Bhai Mardana, had been travelling for many moons now, spreading the message of peace and compassion. After crossing several little villages and large towns, they reached a place where the land ended and the ocean began. Their next destination was an island, somewhere in the middle of the vast ocean. It would be an expedition that would take them three days and three nights.

Mardana stared at the waters lapping the shore where they stood and gulped. *How are we going to cross this,* he wondered. The blue waters stretched endlessly before them with no land in sight. "Is there even an island somewhere in this enormous ocean? How will we get there?" he mumbled.

Worried about what Guru Nanak might think, he kept his concerns to himself. Guru Nanak's calm voice cut through his turbulent thoughts, almost as if reading Mardana's mind, "We will be travelling on the back of a large fish," he said.

As Mardana watched, the smooth ripples turned into uncontrollable waves that splashed everywhere. A dark shape approached the shore. It became bigger as it drew closer. Through the next wave, they could make out a shape so huge it cast a dark shadow over them. Finally, a giant fish emerged onto the shore.

Mardana was shocked. *This was no fish. It was a monstrous beast.* As it floated on the waters, its mammoth scales shimmered like a rainbow. It had a dreadful, pointed face with large, beady eyes and a mouth so large that it seemed like it could swallow a human in one go. Guru Nanak and Bala climbed onto the back of the fish and Mardana had no choice but to follow.

The beast plunged its large face into the ocean and began swimming. Mardana shifted in his seat, still apprehensive of travelling on a monster fish. Bala reassured him, "You must have faith. This is a creation of God. We are with Guru Nanak, we must trust him." Mardana sighed, took out his *rebab*, and played some music to calm himself.

As the sun set, the beast raised its head and to Mardana's horror opened its giant mouth. *Would it eat them*? Inside its mouth, however, was an offering of food. Bala and Mardana were very pleased. Guru Nanak then asked the creature with a smile, "Who are you?"

"You do not know who I am, but I know you, Guru Nanak. I was destined to meet you again," the fish said. "I was a human in my previous life and worked for you. I was very lazy then, because of which, I was born into this form. I have been searching for you, swimming through the seven oceans, hoping to one day be of service to you and redeem my soul."

As Bala and Mardana watched, Guru Nanak smiled and blessed him. The creature was no beast, but a soul trapped in the body of a giant, monstrous fish.

Three days and three nights later, they reached the island. The fish left Guru Nanak, Bala, and Mardana at the shore and bid them goodbye. He swam away, leaving behind his troubles and the burdens of his past. Guru Nanak had freed his soul with his blessing. The giant fish had found redemption and fulfilled his destiny.

Meanwhile, back at the island, Mardana was feeling remorse for losing his faith, and allowing it to disappear in a whirlpool of doubt. He had forgotten that all creatures created by God should be judged by their deeds and not their appearance.

Guru Nanak looked at him with a smile, "I accept you as you are. Bhai Mardana, Bhai Bala, you are my companions."

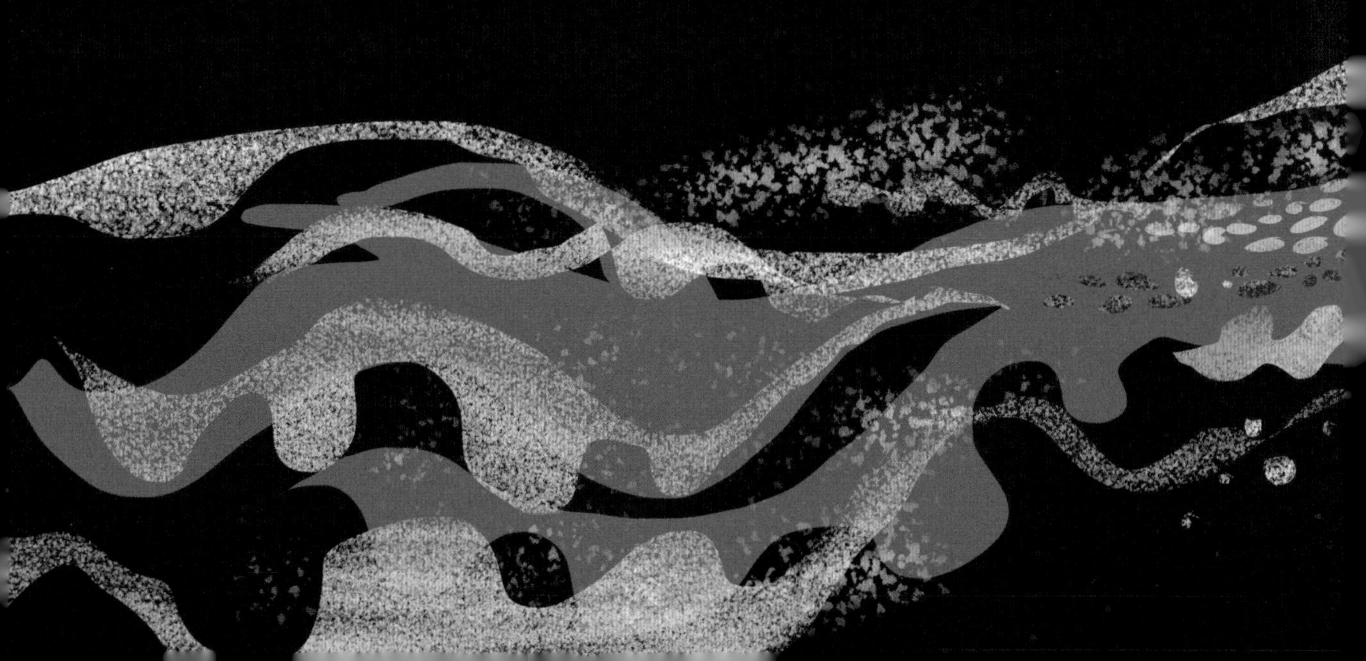

They walked away together,
embarking on many more journeys
of enlightenment – in the north, east,
far south, and the far, far west.

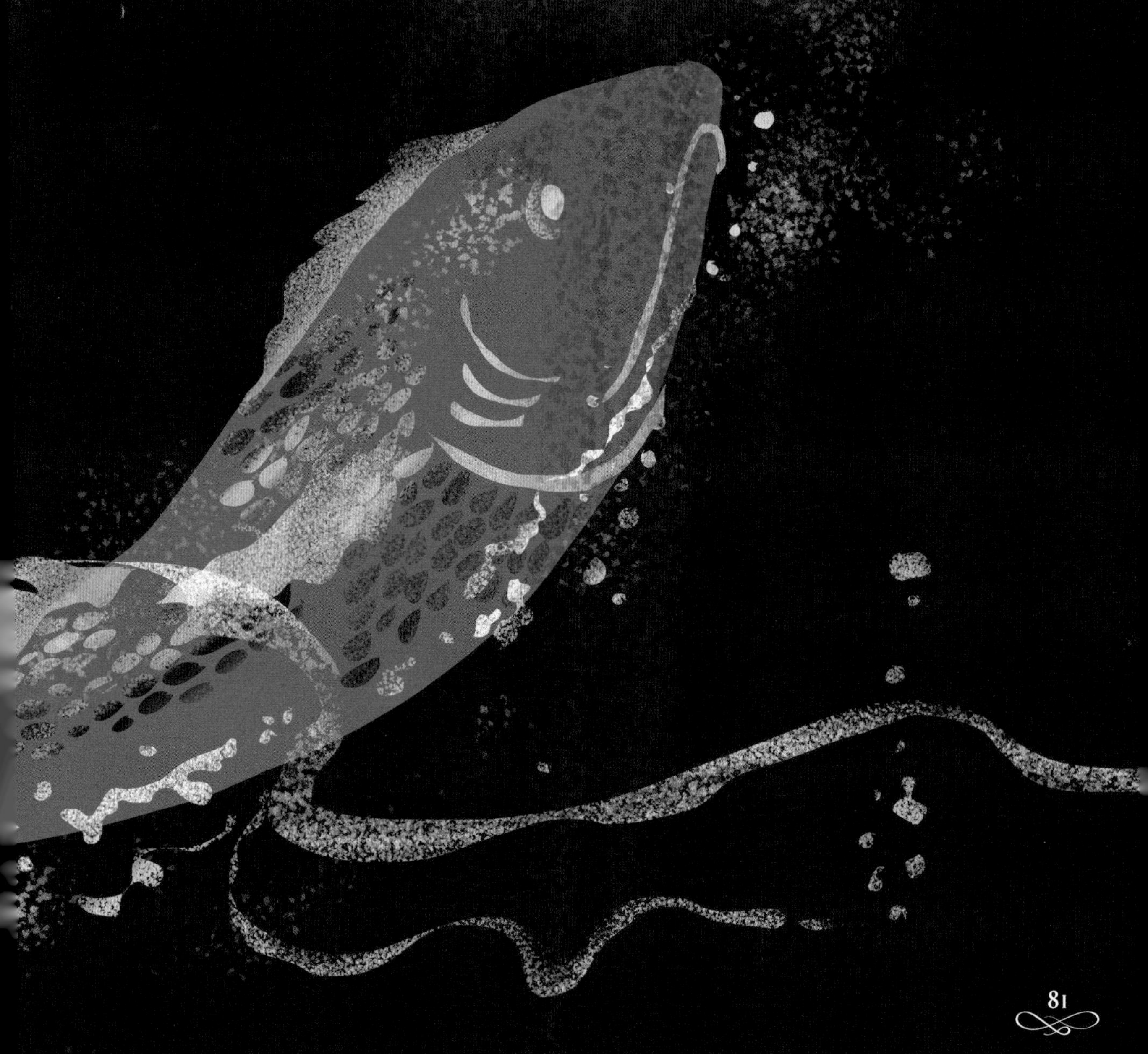

The Wily Fox

A folk tale from Assam

There was once a fox who roamed the lush, forested hills of Assam. One night, in the hopes of finding a meal, the fox made his way down to a village on the edge of the forest. He could see the faint flicker of oil lamps in the distance. He crept from one house to the next, avoiding the patches of light from the tiny windows. He hoped to find at least one unlocked chicken coop, but luck was not on his side.

Now desperate, the fox turned a corner and spotted a farmer putting out a basket of *pithas*, or rice cakes, to cool them. The aroma of toasted rice and *gur*, or jaggery, made him even more hungry and he couldn't wait to eat them. The farmer had barely gone back into his house that the fox pounced on the basket. He stuck his head in and gobbled up the *pithas*, barely pausing for a breath. He even ate the banana leaf at the bottom of the basket. He tried to reach every little crumb and, in doing so, broke the bottom of the rickety old basket. Startled, he tried to pull his head out, but the basket was stuck on his neck like a collar. Try as he might, the basket it would not come off.

It put an end to his days of raiding villages. He would get caught in fences, be spotted by people, and ever so often, when he ran, he would trip over the basket. To top it all, the other animals teased him so much that he decided to move to a nearby forest.

The animals there had never seen a fox like him and looked at the basket around his neck in wonder. The fox basked in this new-found attention. He soon started swaying while walking, shaking the basket around his neck, so that he would look even more impressive. The other animals began calling him "the necklaced one".

One day, while strutting through the forest, the fox met two tiger cubs who were feasting on meat and had a devious idea.

"Greetings, young cubs," he called out. "I have come to meet your parents. Where are they?" He looked around cautiously and added, "Surely they heard of my arrival and fled, leaving you young ones to deal with me."

The cubs, caught by surprise, replied in meek voices, "Our parents have gone to hunt."

"Well that is what they would like you to believe," the fox said in a rather pompous fashion. "A long time ago, your father took a loan, and never paid me back. I have come to collect it, but I am tired of waiting. I will return tomorrow," he said.

Eyeing their meat, he added, "For now, I will eat your meal as payment." He then gobbled up their food and left. From that day on, the fox visited the cubs every day around the time their parents went hunting and ate all their food. Soon, the cubs grew thin and weak.

Concerned by the drastic change, their mother, the tigress, asked the tiger stay back and observe them. The devious fox arrived like clockwork for his stolen meal. The tiger jumped out of his hiding place and roared, startling the fox who ran away. The tiger chased him, but the fox was agile. He scampered through the bushes and spotted a small, sturdy tree with branches that were split into a "V". He had an idea.

He jumped through the branches, narrowly slipping through them. The tiger was not so lucky and found himself trapped. He struggled and clawed at the tree, but could not break free. As the sun rose the next morning, the exhausted tiger knew his time was up. He roared one last time and died. The tigress rushed to the tree and found the tiger. The fox was there as well.

"I have vanquished the tiger," the fox said. "This is the power I possess and you will suffer the same fate if you do not pay back what your husband owed me."

"I do not have any money. I cannot pay you," the tigress replied.

"Then you will have to serve me", he replied. "Bring me food every day, and do whatever I ask, or you will end up like your husband as well."

Scared and helpless, the tigress agreed. Every day, she would hunt for her children and the nasty fox. As the years passed, the cubs grew up watching their mother struggle to feed the fox. He even followed them across the river to their new, larger den and insisted on staying with them. Annoyed with their uninvited guest, the tigers started plotting ways to get rid of him.

Then, one night, the fox sat outside the den, gazing at the moon, which looked like a large pearl in the sky. Suddenly, he heard howls in the distance. It was the other foxes and jackals who lived in the forest. Something awoke inside him and he could not stop himself. He threw his head back and howled. The cacophony woke the tigers who saw the fox howling into the night.

The tigers realized that he was no fearsome beast, but a silly fox. They sprang on him and, in the blink of an eye, gobbled him up. They, then, swore that no one would ever fool them again.

The Saviour Spider

A story from the Quran

Night had fallen and craggy mountains loomed over a narrow, winding path. Prophet Muhammad and Abu Bakr, his companion, hurried along. With every other step, Abu Bakr would look back to see if anyone was following them.

The two friends had left their home in Mecca and were on the run. They were being chased relentlessly by the Quraysh tribe, which controlled trade in the city and believed in a different god. Prophet Muhammad and his followers worshipped Allah and for this, they had been driven from their homes. Fortunately, the rulers of Medina, a desert oasis surrounded by mountains, had extended an invitation to them.

The Prophet's followers had made it across. Now, the Prophet and Abu Bakr were on their way to Medina. They left in the depths of the night and took the longer road, travelling through rocky and rough mountainous paths.

They scrambled over rocks in the darkness, trying to stay one step ahead of the Quraysh, who were hard on their heels. They searched for shelter, a safe place where they could spend the night. That's when they spotted a cave. *This would be a good place to stay*, Abu Bakr thought. The two entered it and sat in the darkness. Suddenly, they heard a noise. Abu Bakr froze. It was a search party sent by the Quraysh. He looked at the Prophet and worried for his safety.

The Prophet smiled. There was nothing to be worried about.

As the search party drew closer, a female spider at the entrance of the cave began spinning a web.

She started with a single silky thread and jumped back and forth across the mouth of the cave. She moved up and down and sideways, and did not stop. Soon, a web hung over the entrance, grey, dusty, and knotted.

The search party now reached the cave and stood outside the entrance. They spotted the spider web, dense and intricate. There was no way someone would have been able to hide inside, for webs, they had heard, only formed in unoccupied places. So, the Quraysh abandoned their search.

Today, that cave, named Jabal Thawr, is a place of great importance to Muslims across the world.

After all, it is here that a tiny spider's frail web saved the lives of the Prophet and Abu Bakr.

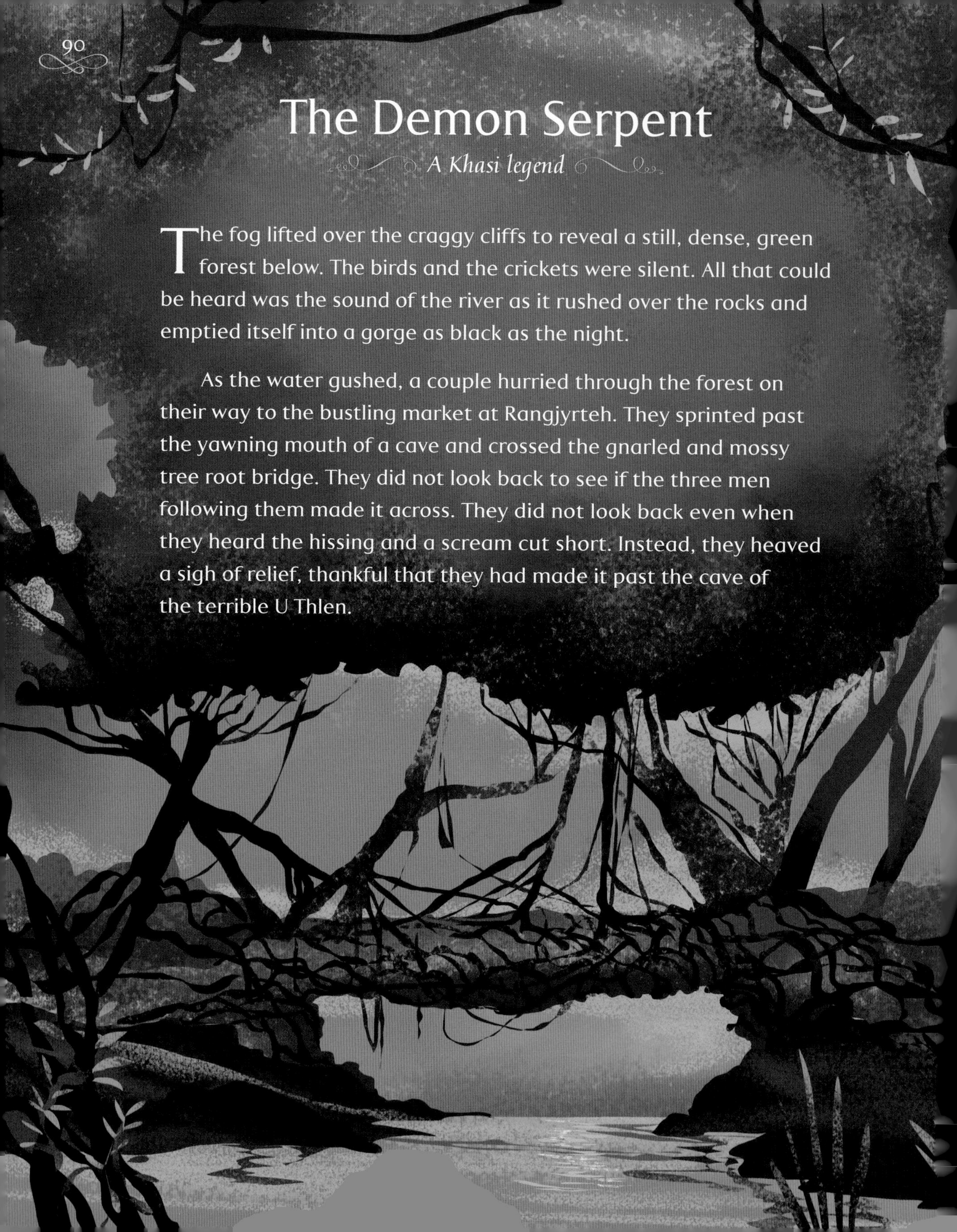

The Demon Serpent

A Khasi legend

The fog lifted over the craggy cliffs to reveal a still, dense, green forest below. The birds and the crickets were silent. All that could be heard was the sound of the river as it rushed over the rocks and emptied itself into a gorge as black as the night.

As the water gushed, a couple hurried through the forest on their way to the bustling market at Rangjyrteh. They sprinted past the yawning mouth of a cave and crossed the gnarled and mossy tree root bridge. They did not look back to see if the three men following them made it across. They did not look back even when they heard the hissing and a scream cut short. Instead, they heaved a sigh of relief, thankful that they had made it past the cave of the terrible U Thlen.

The giant demon serpent, his fanged mouth wide open and tail stretching deep into the cave, would lie in wait for a human to walk past. He only attacked those who travelled alone or in groups of three or five. He could grow in size to fill the cave or become as tiny as a worm.

No one knew where this monstrous creature had come from. Some believed that he was once a human, who had gone mad with grief after the murder of his son and turned into a serpent. Others whispered that he was the son of an evil fairy, taught to hate humans. It didn't matter where he came from or who he was, because U Thlen had an insatiable appetite for human blood.

As more and more people vanished, the villagers prayed for help, first to the gods and then the demons. They were told that only U Suidnoh, the disappearing demon, would be able to help them.

U Suidnoh lived in the sacred forest of Lait-rngew and agreed to help the villagers. First, he took U Lei Shillong's blessings, for he needed the mountain god's permission to kill any creature who lived in the area. Then, he asked the villagers to collect all the plump goats and pigs they could find. Finally, he bore a hole through the roof of U Thlen's cave.

Every day, he called out to the serpent through the hole in the roof. "Uncle, uncle," he would shout. "I have brought you food. Open your mouth so that I can feed you." U Thlen, thinking someone was offering him a human as a sacrifice, would open his jaws wide.

U Suidnoh would drop the animal through the hole and the serpent would swallow it whole, thinking it was a human being. The mighty U Thlen never thought anyone would be brave enough to fool him. This went on for months.

The villagers soon grew tired of collecting goats and pigs. It was a tough task to find the plumpest ones. They grumbled and complained, but U Suidnoh smiled. “Be patient,” he told them, “be patient.”

One day, after many months had passed, he asked U Ramhah, the giant, to forge a massive pair of tongs. When it was ready, he placed a large piece of iron in the heart of a fire. Once the iron had become so hot it turned white, U Suidnoh carried it to the cave.

“Uncle, uncle,” he called out through the hole in the roof. “I have brought you food. Open your mouth so that I can feed you.”

U Thlen heard him and slithered towards the hole. He had grown lazy and unwary over the months, and opened his jaws and waited. U Suidnoh flung the iron into his mouth.

The monster roared and writhed in pain as the iron roasted his insides. His screams echoed through the land and the villagers trembled. The ground shook, as the serpent twisted and turned, and split open to form deep, dark gorges that cut through the forest. Then, just as suddenly, there was silence.

U Suidnoh climbed into the cave and saw the serpent lying there, motionless. U Thlen had been defeated.

That evening, U Suidnoh called villagers from across the land to the top of the highest cliff. Fine mist, like a white veil, hung in the air. The river ended in a waterfall here, emptying itself into the gorge below. First, U Suidnoh hacked the serpent into little pieces, handing every villager one to eat. Then, he burnt the rest in a large bonfire at the edge of the waterfall. This place is today called Dain-Thlen, or the place where U Thlen was cut.

"Do not leave even a morsel," he warned the people. "Either eat it or burn it. Leave nothing behind." So saying, the demon disappeared.

An old woman decided to save the meat for her son who could not come to the feast. She returned to her thatched hut and stored it in a pot, covering it with leaves. She soon forgot about it.

One day, she heard a strange voice calling to her, urging her to open the pot. When she did, she fell back in fear. A tiny snake lay there, curled up in the leaves. It opened its eyes and hissed, "Old woman, feed me and I will shower you with treasures. You will be rich."

The woman trembled. It was U Thlen. He was alive. She realized why U Suidnoh had warned them and insisted that no one leave any piece of the serpent behind. *What was she to do*? She turned to run out and warn the villagers, but the snake hissed, his voice now stronger and malicious: "If you tell anyone, your entire family will die. But, if you bring me a human to eat, you will be the richest person in all the land."

Shaking, the woman fell to the ground and agreed. U Thlen's reign of terror had begun once more.

It is said that U Thlen lives on even today, preying on people's greed to survive. He devours humans and their souls, seeking revenge on all who tried to kill him.

The Hungry Bear

A story from Punjab

The big brown bear stomped through the forest searching for food when he caught a whiff of the most wonderful scent. He had never smelt anything like it. Now bears are a good sort, though they can be inquisitive and, on occasion, quite greedy. This bear was also hungry, so he used his masterful nose to follow the delicious aroma until he reached a tiny cottage. He peered inside and saw an old woman and man bickering over a large brass pot.

"If you want even a morsel of this *khichdi*, you will bring me a bundle of wood, else I will not be able to cook tomorrow," the woman told the man.

The man grumbled, "I am old now and I may die before I even see tomorrow's sun." But his wife was adamant.

The grumpy man got up and walked into the forest to gather wood. As he collected the sticks, the bear ambled up to him and said, "That is a lot of wood."

"Well," said the old man, "My wife will only give me the *khichdi* she made if I return with a big bundle of wood. Her *khichdi* is the best in all the land. She even adds a dollop of creamy butter and heavenly spices."

The bear, ever an incurable glutton, felt his stomach grumble. He asked, "Will she give me a share of the *khichdi* if I bring a bundle of wood as well?"

The old man perked up, "Yes, she will definitely give you some *khichdi*."

"Tell your wife to keep the pot hot. I will be there in an instant," the bear said and started gathering wood at the speed of light.

Meanwhile, the old man sprinted to his house and relayed the incident to his wife. The crafty woman remarked sharply, “I bet you did not settle on the share the bear will have. They have huge appetites, you know. He will lick the pot clean before we even finish our first helping.”

“Well, we must get a head start then,” the old man said. They sat down to eat the *khichdi*, each taking turns to remind the other to save some for the bear.

“Save some for the bear, dear,” said the man as he slurped his bowl of *khichdi*.

“Remember to keep the bear’s share!” reminded the woman, with a nudge.

They soon ate every drop of the *khichdi.* "What will we do now? The bear must be on his way here with the wood!" exclaimed the old man peering into the pot, which was now empty.

"Let's hide," she replied, "He will leave if he sees that no one is home."

The tired bear arrived with a large bundle of wood. The cottage still smelt wonderful and as the bear walked in, his stomach growled with hunger. He saw the *khichdi* pot and found it empty. He could not believe it. He stuck his paw in. Perhaps there was a little *khichdi* left. There was nothing, not even a morsel. The pot had been licked clean. Furious, he turned the house upside down searching for food, but could not find anything to eat.

He then peered out of the window, and spotted a tree with golden pears that hung heavily over the yard, which belonged to the rich orchard owner next door. The couple were only allowed to have the fruit that fell on their land.

Ecstatic, the hungry bear ran towards the tree, climbed up, and started popping the juicy pears into his mouth, when a thought struck him. *What if I sell these pears to other bears and use that money to buy* khichdi?

It was a fantastic idea, he thought. He grabbed the empty *khichdi* pot and started filling it with ripe, syrupy sweet pears. Whenever he grabbed an unripe one, he would say, "No one would pay a *paisa* for these, but it would be a pity to let them go to waste." Then, he would pop them into his mouth.

The old woman and man watched the bear through the attic window. The attic had gathered dust over the years, which itched the woman's nose. "*Ah ... ah ... ah... Achchooooooo,*" she sneezed.

The thunderous sound shook the house and echoed for miles. The bear heard it and thought it was a gun. Trembling with fear, he dropped the pot and fled into the forest to save his life. The old couple could not believe their luck. They gathered up the pears and had a delicious dessert that evening.

What of the hungry bear?
All he ended up with was
a tummy ache because of
all those unripe pears.
He never ever went looking
for *khichdi* ever again.

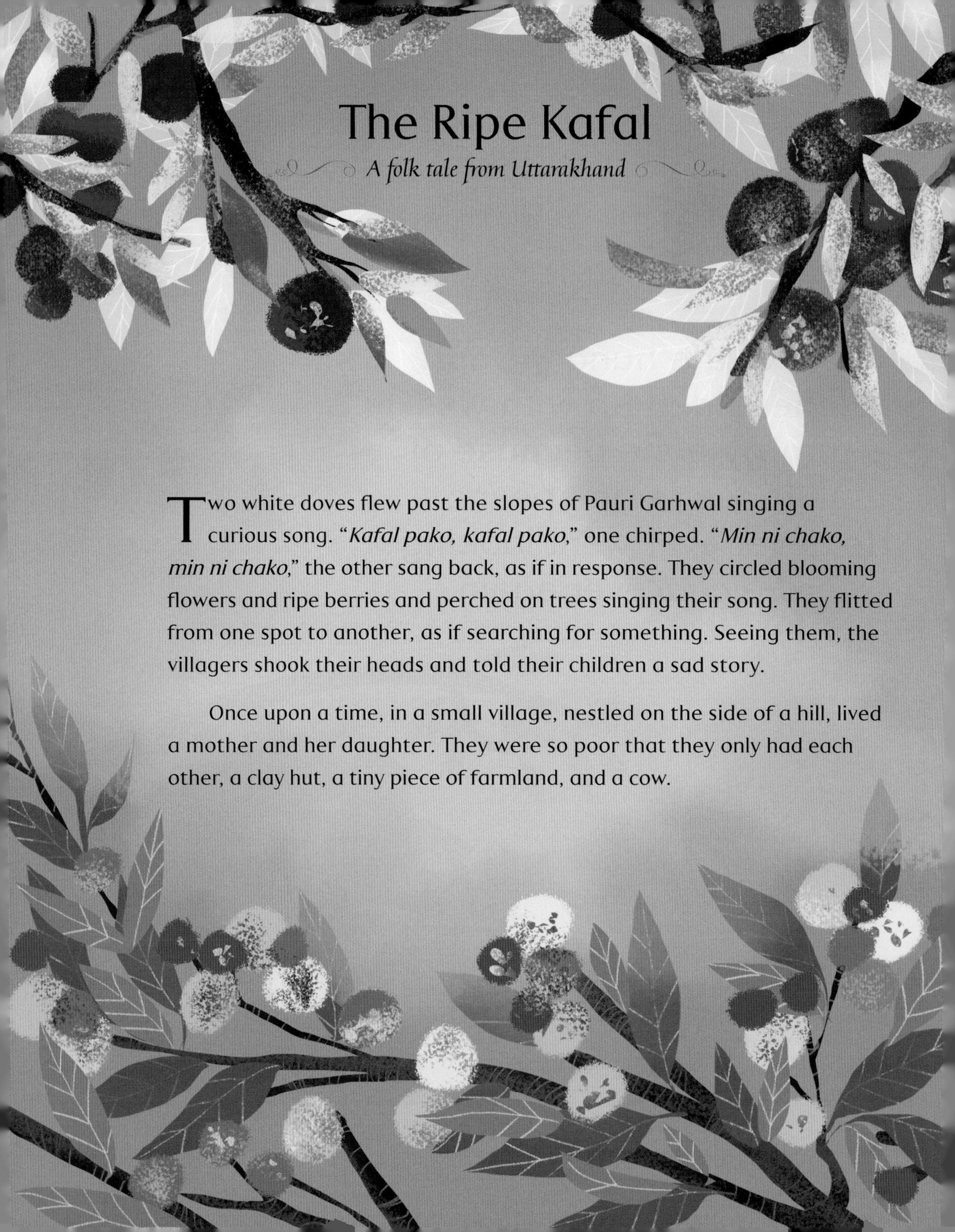

The Ripe Kafal

A folk tale from Uttarakhand

Two white doves flew past the slopes of Pauri Garhwal singing a curious song. "*Kafal pako, kafal pako,*" one chirped. "*Min ni chako, min ni chako,*" the other sang back, as if in response. They circled blooming flowers and ripe berries and perched on trees singing their song. They flitted from one spot to another, as if searching for something. Seeing them, the villagers shook their heads and told their children a sad story.

Once upon a time, in a small village, nestled on the side of a hill, lived a mother and her daughter. They were so poor that they only had each other, a clay hut, a tiny piece of farmland, and a cow.

The harvest had been sparse one year and they did not have enough food to eat. When the summer month of *Jeth* finally came around, the mother heaved a sigh of relief. She had been watching the bright red, sweet and sour *kafal* fruit growing in the jungle. *Surely they would be ripe by now.* They could pick some and sell them in the market. They would keep the leftovers for themselves.

The next day, the mother and her daughter went into the jungle and gathered the *kafal* in two baskets. The little girl was excited and could not wait to bite into the juicy berries.

They returned home and carefully covered the baskets. The mother stepped out to get fodder for the cow and, as she was leaving, told her daughter, "Keep an eye on the *kafal* and complete your chores. Don't eat them until I come home." The little girl promised that she would do as she was told.

As she waited for her mother, the little girl completed all her chores. Every once in a while, she peered into the baskets to look at the fruits. They were ripe, delicious, and had a wonderful fragrance. She was famished, but she resisted. After all, she had promised her mother.

The mother returned after a few hours and saw the daughter curled up in a corner. It looked like she was fast asleep. She glanced at the *kafal* and was shocked to see that it was half of what she had left. Had her daughter eaten the fruit?

Disappointed that the child had broken the promise, the mother went over to wake her up, but something was not right. Her daughter was cold as ice. She was not even breathing. To her horror, she realized that her child had died in her sleep because of hunger. The mother wept as she cradled the little girl's lifeless body.

Soon, the sun set and the evening mist settled into the hills. The mist entered their hut and surrounded the child. As it cleared, the girl transformed into a little white dove. She fluttered wings and looked at the weeping mother. Then, she sang a sad song and flew out the window.

The mother glanced at the baskets and realized that they were full once again. She did not know this at the time, but *kafal* loses its volume because of heat during the day. Then it returns to its ripened form in the cool evening breeze. Now all alone, the heartbroken mother lay down and closed her eyes. The next day, she too disappeared.

Some believe that she transformed into a dove as well and flew away into the hills, in search of her beloved daughter.

Even today, a pair of doves
can be seen circling *kafal*
trees in the summer. One sings,
kafal pako, or the *kafal* are ripe.
To which the other responds,
min ni chakho,
or I did not taste them.

The Great Protector

A tale from the Bhagavata Purana

The great *asura* king Hiranyakashipu stood on the tips of his toes on the top of the Mandarachal mountain. He ignored the sharp, icy wind that cut through the air like a knife. He closed his eyes, joined his hands, and prayed to Lord Brahma, the creator. He wanted to become stronger than all the *asuras* and *devas* that lived in heaven, on earth, and in the netherworld.

So strong was his devotion that fire burst from his crown and burnt the earth. The lakes and rivers dried and mountains quaked. No one had ever prayed to Brahma like this before. Frightened, the *devas* rushed to the creator, begging him to intervene.

Brahma appeared before the *asura* king. "What do you desire?" he asked, smiling.

Hiranyakashipu bowed and said, "I want to control the *asuras* and the *devas*. I wish for no weapon, wet or dry, to kill me. No *deva*, *asura*, human, or animal should be able to kill me, during day or night, neither inside nor outside."

Brahma, pleased with the *asura* king's penance, blessed him with these boons – something he had never done before – and disappeared.

Hiranyakashipu returned to his kingdom, more powerful than ever, and ruled over all the worlds. He could take on the form of the sun or the moon and control the skies. He could become the wind and tear through the earth and the heaven.

As Hiranyakashipu devastated the three worlds, he grew arrogant and started believing that he was God. Scared for their lives, the *asuras* and the *devas* started worshipping him, except for one.

Prahlada, Hiranyakashipu's eldest son, was the opposite of his father. He was kind, considerate, and wise beyond his years. Most of all, he worshipped Lord Vishnu, the preserver of all beings. The *asura* king did everything to change Prahlada's mind. He banished him from the palace and threatened him with death as well. The young boy's faith in Vishnu, however, remained unshakeable.

One day, the *asura* king had enough. He called for Prahlada. This was his last chance. If his son continued to pray to Vishnu, Hiranyakashipu announced, he would kill him. The boy entered the palace and stood before his father.

"Where is Vishnu, this god of yours? I can't see him. The only god I see is me, sitting in front of you?" Hiranyakashipu thundered.

"He is everywhere," replied the young boy, his voice, calm and soft.

"Where?" shouted Hiranyakashipu. "Is he here?" he roared, pointing at a pillar. "Is your Vishnu in this pillar?"

Prahlada replied, with a smile, "Yes. I see him there as well, father."

Furious at Prahlada's response, the powerful *asura* punched the pillar. He then walked over to his son, sword in hand. "Let's see how Vishnu will save you now," he said with growl.

Hiranyakashipu lifted his sword and was about to strike when the ground trembled. A large rumble shook the palace and shattered the pillar. There, in its ruins, stood a strange being. It had a lion's head, fierce, amber eyes, and a mane as golden as the sun. It had hundreds of arms, which ended in claws, as sharp as swords. Massive tusks sprouted from either side of the face and its mouth opened in a snarl ready to devour the evil king.

The creature's name was Narasimha, an incarnation of Vishnu, born to destroy Hiranyakashipu. It shook its menacing head and roared.

At that moment, the sun disappeared behind the moon, casting an odd crimson hue across the earth. It was neither day nor night. Alarmed, people wept in fear and the *devas* and *asuras* emerged from their worlds.

Hiranyakashipu stared at the creature before him and felt fear for the first time. He raised his sword to attack it, but Narasimha laughed. It struck the king with its gold mace and then carried him to the palace's threshold as if he were a little doll. It laid him on its lap and roared. The terrifying sound ripped through the palace. Then, Narasimha tore the king apart with its claws.

Hiranyakashipu was dead, killed by neither a human nor an animal, but a man-lion. He was neither inside nor outside, but on the threshold of his palace at a time that was neither day nor night.

The people of earth, the *devas* of the heavens, and the *asuras* of the netherworlds heaved a sigh of relief and celebrated the tyrant's death. They were free at last.

Soon after, Prahlada was crowned king and he ruled with wisdom and compassion.

The Clever Crab

A story from the Panchatantra

There once was a pelican who used his beak and claws to snap up the fish that lived in a lake with crystal-clear waters, nestled deep within the Aravallis. One day, the fish came up with a plan, "Let's not go out during the day. Let's hide deep in the waters and go up to the surface at night."

The pelican, though, was clever. He would wait for moonlight, spot the silver flash of fins, open his mouth, and dive. Then, up he would fly with the night's catch clutched in his beak.

Many years passed and the pelican's reign was supreme. Then came a day when he dived into the lake ... and his prey escaped. You see, the pelican had grown old and slow. All he could catch now were crickets and they were not as delicious as the fish.

One beautiful spring day, the pelican eyed the fish playing in the lake and longed for the days when he was quick to catch them. He moped and complained all day. "Fly around with an open mouth and hope a stupid cricket flies in. Is this any way to live?" he lamented with a scowl on his face.

A crab scuttled by just then and asked him, "What is wrong, grandfather pelican? Why are you sad?"

The pelican looked at her and blinked. "Why?" he started slowly, plotting. "I spied some humans coming this way. They plan to cut down our mountains, drain our lake, and cart away all the fish."

"What?" the crab cried in shock.

The pelican nodded. "It breaks my heart, knowing our home will be destroyed. Think about the poor little fish."

"We must warn them," the crab said, scurrying towards the lake in a hurry.

On receiving the news, the fish formed a council. After much debate, they went to the pelican who had a solution. "Past those mountains, over a river, there lies a lake, even bigger and clearer than ours. Why don't you hop in my beak and I'll carry you over there? Maybe take a few of you every day?"

"So you can eat us all up?" asked a sceptical fish.

The pelican shook his head. "No, no. Of course not," he lied. "I wish to help you! Though if it scares you, you could latch onto my feathers with your mouths, and let go when we reach the new lake."

It had been many years since the pelican had been a real threat, and so the fish agreed in the end.

Every day, the pelican would take the fish, not to a lake, but a plateau. After landing, he would shake himself so hard that the tired fish would fall off. Then, he would eat them one by one. This continued for many weeks. Soon, the pelican stopped looking scrawny and the little crab grew suspicious.

What if grandfather pelican takes the fish and then eats them? It was a horrible thought. Worried, the crab hurried forward and asked. "Why don't you take me along today?" The pelican agreed.

Climbing onto the bird's shoulders, the crab wrapped her pincers around his neck. The pelican took off and started flying. After a while, they still had not reached the lake. The crab squinted against the sun, but could not see anything. Instead, she spotted a plateau, covered in hundreds, maybe even thousands, of fish bones. The pelican flew over the plateau and as always shook himself. Today, he would make a meal of the crab.

The crab was ready for the pelican's crafty tricks. She squeezed her pincers shut, wrapping them tightly around the bird's neck. The pelican struggled to break free, but the crab only tightened her hold. They crashed.

The crab tottered to her feet. The pelican lay there moaning and groaning. The crab ignored him and scuttled back to the lake. There she told the remaining fish what she had seen and what had happened. They mourned their friends, but were relieved that they were free of the pelican at last. They could now live in the lake without any fear.

As for the pelican, no one really knows what happened to him, for the fish and crab never saw him again.

The Tiger Man

A folk tale from the Sumi tribe of Nagaland

Tucked deep in the heart of Nagaland's lush valleys, there once stood a tiny village fringed by mountains. In it, along with his small family, lived an ordinary man with an extraordinary soul.

Hutovi Ayemi, as he was known, could speak to spirits and the souls of the dead who lived in the forests. Every day, members of Hutovi's tribe gathered at his hut to pass onto him their wishes and messages to the spirits.

"Tell *aza*, my mother, that her grandson has learnt to crawl and sit up all by himself," one would say.

"My paddy field has begun to dry up. Would you ask the nature goddess to revive it with rain?" another would ask.

The requests kept coming, although no one really knew just how Hutovi communicated with the departed souls.

The secret was his magical soul. Every evening, as the bright red sun sank into the horizon, making way for the glow of the moonlight, Hutovi lay down to sleep. Then, mystical forces came into play. His soul would awaken with a jolt, leave his body, and take the form of a majestic tiger.

The fearsome and powerful creature roamed the forests in the dark of the night and travelled to faraway lands beyond the village, running free past snowy cliffs, through rocky ravines, glittering streams, and meadows sprinkled with wildflowers. Along the way, he would stop to speak with the spirits of the forest and his community of fellow beasts. Then, finally, when hungry, he would make his way back to the village, and feast on a cow, goat, or one of the other animals reared by the tribe.

At daybreak, when the very first rays of the sun warmed the earth, he returned to his human body. Hutovi would wake up, get dressed, and head out to the fields like any ordinary farmer. His son often joined him to help plough the farmland and feed their herd of goats.

One day, alarmed at their disappearing livestock, the tribespeople held a meeting. "I know the beast that is responsible for this!" cried one of them, "I've seen it with my very eyes!"

"I've seen it too – a bloodthirsty tiger with a hide brighter than the flames!" exclaimed another.

"I heard it lives in the forests of Zunheboto," chimed in a third

As they talked, the tribespeople got angrier and angrier. "It is only a matter of time before this tiger grows hungry for human flesh. We must kill the beast before it kills us," they said. After much deliberation, they decided it was time to hunt the tiger.

That night, unaware of the villagers' plans, Hutovi went to bed as usual. His soul, in its tiger form, leapt out of the hut. He was about to disappear into the forest when he heard the trees and bushes rustle. As he turned, the tribespeople, armed with flaming torches, sickles, bows, and arrows, sprang out of their hiding places.

Startled, the tiger let out a powerful roar and darted towards the forest, scrambling through the rugged terrain in a frantic search for cover. The poor creature's efforts were in vain. A few tribespeople armed with bows, hiding in the forest, caught up and shot him with poisoned arrows.

The following morning, as the village celebrated the death of the tiger, Hutovi's weakened soul struggled to make his way home. In the hut, he lay sick and paralyzed. The soul had been unable to return to Hutovi's human body.

Later that day, a few villagers gathered at Hutovi's hut hoping to convey their messages to the spirits in the forest, only to find his body frozen and motionless.

"What is the matter? Why don't you speak up? Won't you talk to the spirits for us?" they cried together. When there was no response, the villagers realized that their link to the world of spirits and magic had been lost forever.

Panic-stricken and awash in grief, they began to wail. "How are we ever going to live without talking to the spirits? Who will guide us? Whom will we go to in times of happiness or sorrow?"

At that very moment, Hutovi spoke, "You do not know what you have done. You have committed a grave sin, my dear friends. The tiger you chased and killed mercilessly was a part of my soul. We were one, as nature and humankind are one. We cannot survive without each other."

"I am now going to sleep, to rest eternally. But these powers shall pass down to my son in time. Be kind to him and kinder to nature, and you will rediscover your connection with the spirits." Then, Hutovi lay back and closed his eyes. He died soon after.

The villagers wept that day, ashamed of what they had done. They laid Hutovi's body in a coffin, and in a final act of love and reverence, covered it with the hide of the slain tiger before burying him. They hoped that in the afterlife, his human and tiger forms would reunite and his soul would live on forever.

From that day on, the tribe started cherishing and respecting nature and its wondrous creations.

Their devotion bore fruit and Hutovi's words came true. Soon, his son rekindled the tribe's connection with the spirits of the forest. He carried on the task of communicating with them, as did the generations that followed him.

Wrath of the Witch

A myth from the Kol tribe of Central India

Once upon a time in the tiny town of Jhinjhingarh lived a farmer who wanted to sow a crop that was extra special. With great care, he cleared his field and planted the *kutki* root. This bitter herb with violet flowers was known to cure many health conditions.

He tended to his crop day and night, until one day all the work paid off. His field had a fine crop of long-eared *kutki*, with its upright leaves and tiny spikes that were several shades of violet. When the wind blew, the crop would sway and the sight made the farmer swell with pride.

One day, an old lady walking past the field spotted the *kutki* flowers. Mesmerized, she walked through the field and crushed some of the plants with her feet, quite by accident. The farmer, who was nearby, started scolding the woman.

"How dare you destroy my herbs, you horrid person," he yelled. "Get away from my field." The woman was shocked, as the farmer kept berating her. Suffice to say, he was very, very rude. He only stopped shouting after she left the field.

What the farmer did not know was that the woman was a witch who lived in the forest. She wielded great magical powers and now sought revenge.

That night, she returned to the field and plucked a few *kukti* flowers. Crushing them with her fingers, she whispered a few magical words. As the crumpled petals fell to the ground, they transformed into tiny, black, six-legged creatures.

She continued crushing the flowers and with every petal that touched the field, the creatures multiplied. Soon, they were everywhere. They ate all of the *kutki* – the flowers, leaves, stems, everything. Satisfied, the witch walked away into the forest.

She had no idea of the little monsters she had just created. Once they devoured the herbs, the creatures wanted more. Some crawled their way to the fields in the north, others to the south and the east, while the rest went west. That is how cockroaches came to be and spread to the rest of the world.

As for the farmer, the following day he was devastated at the sight of his field. He had learnt his lesson and from that day on treated everyone with respect.

Vulture of the Vindhyas

A tale from the Kishkindha Kandam

Sampati, the king of vultures, and his younger brother Jatayu soared through the sky. They were racing each other, flying higher and higher, inching towards the scorching sun. Jatayu was ahead, jubilant that he was winning against his elder brother. He looked back and saw Sampati gaining speed. They were so high that the blue ocean, green forests, and white snow-capped mountains seemed like mere splotches in the distance.

Jatayu suddenly felt his wings burning. *He was too close to the sun.* He became unsteady and started losing his balance. Seeing this, Sampati flew between Jatayu and the sun to protect his brother. He spread open his wings, shielding Jatayu, but the sun's heat ravaged his feathers, burning them up, and blinded him.

Dizzy and injured, both brothers fell to the earth. Sampati plunged into the lush hills of the Vindhyas. His dear brother was nowhere in sight. As days passed, Sampati's eyesight returned, but only partially. Now wingless, he spent his days roaming the low, rolling hills from where he could see the ocean. There were moments of despair when all he wanted was death, for he had lost all that he loved. Then, an encounter with a learned sage named Nishkara brought him hope.

The sage had heard Sampati's story and said, "You still have purpose. You will regain your wings, eyesight, and strength once you have fulfilled your purpose. You will have to help Prince Rama on his quest to find his wife. Stay here and be patient. You will get back what you have lost after you have fulfilled your destiny."

Time passed and the sage's words felt like a dream. Now old and weary, Sampati spent his days in a cave in the Vindhyas waiting for his son to bring him food. One day, he heard voices, loud and argumentative.

He stepped out and saw a group of monkeys in deep discussion. Some were sitting cross-legged, while others lay on the ground, looking exhausted and defeated. "Let us just lie here until we die," one monkey said, his voice laced with sadness. "We have failed in our duty."

"We have not been able to help Prince Rama find his wife Sita," said another.

Sampati hopped closer as his stomach grumbled. *These monkeys look like they are ready to die. I will just wait here and eat them one by one. They will make an easy meal.*

The monkeys did not notice the vulture and continued talking among themselves. They had travelled many lands and climbed the highest mountains in search of Sita who had been abducted by Ravana, a powerful *asura* king. She had vanished without a trace and they had not been able to find her. Now, at the southernmost end of the land with only the endless ocean in front of them, the monkeys had given up. Disheartened and too afraid to go back to Lord Rama without any news, they had decided to give up their lives.

"Look what happened to Jatayu, he died trying to save Sita. So many creatures have given their lives to help Rama, but we have failed in our duty," another monkey said.

Sampati stopped in his tracks. He could not believe what he just heard. *Were they talking about his younger brother, Jatayu*? *Was he dead*? *How did that happen*?

Aching with grief, Sampati called out, his voice breaking, "Who speaks of the death of my younger brother? I have not heard his name in a long time."

"Please," he said, tears streaming down his face. "I want to know how he died."

The monkeys gathered around the old vulture and told him about Rama, the prince of Ayodhya, who had been exiled for 14 years with his wife Sita and brother Lakshmana. They then told Sampati about Sita's kidnapping and how the brave Jatayu battled Ravana in an attempt to rescue her. It was a fierce clash, they told Sampati, which shook the skies. Ravana was too powerful and Jatayu fell from the sky to his death. The monkeys were now helping Rama find Sita.

Sampati listened to their story and wept for his brother. "I am old and I don't have wings. I have no strength to avenge my dear brother, but I can help you and your Prince Rama."

The monkeys were astounded. They gathered closer and listened as Sampati told them a strange tale of a maiden his son had seen.

"The lady was in Ravana's chariot. She was struggling, trying to get away. One by one, she dropped her jewellery, crying out for Rama. It has to be Sita. Who else could she have been?" the old vulture told them. "Her silken clothes flew like a flag, as Ravana took her away in his chariot. My son could not save her as the *asura* king is too powerful."

The monkeys got excited. "Where did they go? Please tell us."

"You will find Sita beyond this ocean, in the kingdom of Lanka," Sampati said. As he spoke, a gentle breeze enveloped his body.

He stretched and a pair of powerful wings covered in fiery red feathers sprouted from his shoulders. Sampati had fulfilled his duty, which the Sage Nishkara had spoken of many years ago. Fresh energy coursed through his body. He felt young once again.

"Do not waste time," exclaimed Sampati with renewed vigour as all the apes watched him in awe. "You have been sent here because you are brave, intelligent, and strong. Do not leave any stone unturned. I know you will succeed. This will happen as surely as my wings have grown back."

The army of monkeys roared with joy. The ocean was in front of them and Sita was at the other end of it. They would return with the brave Prince Rama and an army. He would destroy the mighty Ravana in battle and rescue Sita.

Meanwhile, Sampati spread his glorious wings and took flight. Joyous, he felt the breeze in his wings as he soared over the mountains and into the horizon.

The Jackal's New Coat

A story from the Hitopadesha

There once was a wayward jackal who was aimlessly roaming through a village. He walked left and right and then right and left and chanced upon a few large wooden barrels.

"What is inside," he wondered out loud. He slid off the lid with his tail, climbed on to the edge of the barrel, and *PLOP*, fell headfirst in.

Little did he know that the barrel was full of indigo dye. "Ugh! What is this?" he yelled as he splashed and struggled to get out. Suddenly he heard steps and pretended to be dead.

It was the owner of the barrels who had stepped out on hearing the commotion. She gasped at the sight of the barrel without the lid, splotches of blue dye all over the ground, and what seemed to be a "dead" animal floating about. Grumbling, she pulled the jackal out by his tail and left him near the forest.

Seizing the opportunity, the jackal sprinted into the forest, as fast as his four legs could take him. He ran past bush thickets and clusters of sparse trees with flat crowns. He finally stopped at a lake to catch his breath. A group of birds, mice, and rabbits saw him and fled, leaving behind the food they had gathered.

The jackal ignored them. Instead, he leaned towards the lake to drink water and saw his reflection. "*Ahhhhhh*!" he screamed. He was all blue. His face, legs, belly, and tail, everything was blue. He looked around in shock and realized that the animals had run away because of him. Then, looking at all the food they had left behind, he had an idea.

"I have a new coat so now I will only accept the best," he declared and called himself the king of the forest. The other animals thought he was a beast from another land and obeyed him.

His first act as king was to banish all the jackals because he did not want his old friends to recognize him. Then, he made the strongest animals, the tigers, lions, and wolves, his allies and gave them high ranks in his kingdom. They would bring him the best meats, ripest fruits, and freshest water. Soon, the blue jackal grew plump.

Meanwhile, the banished jackals were dejected and hurt. They knew that the blue beast was actually a jackal.

"This blue jackal has rejected his own kind," one jackal said.

Another added, "Not just that, he is now manipulating the others into doing his bidding."

A third chimed in, "The animals in his kingdom must know the truth." So they hatched a plan and decided to meet the next day at the crack of dawn.

The next morning as the plump blue jackal walked to the lake to collect his breakfast, the others hid behind the trees and started howling.

"*Awwwooooooo*," they cried. "*Awwwooooooo*"

The blue jackal stopped, as the call grew louder.

"*Awwwooooooo, Awwwooooooo, Awwwooooooo.*"

They howled in unison and everyone in the blue jackal's kingdom stopped what they were doing.

At that moment, all that the blue jackal wanted to do was howl back, and so he did. He threw his head back and cried, "*Awwwooooooo.*"

The other animals in the forest stared at him in surprise. The jackal's deception had ended. As the tigers and the lions walked towards him, growling, the blue jackal ran for his life. He was never seen in that forest again.

Some say that he lost his
blue coat in the monsoon months.
Now he is plain and ordinary.
So really, he could be anywhere.

The Seven-Legged Beast

A folk tale from Kashmir

There once was a king who was also a great warrior. One day, he decided to hold a grand fair where his powerful and fearless army could show off their skills. It would be held at a large ground near a forest.

The day of the fair dawned and everyone gathered to watch the finest army in all the lands. They *oohed* and *aahed* as the soldiers displayed their strength. The king smiled every time his people cheered, till he spotted his *wazir*, an old man with poor eyesight, who seemed a little distracted.

"What is the matter?" the king asked.

"I am becoming old now and my senses always seem to betray me, your majesty. I thought I heard something rustling among the trees in the forest. I am sure it's nothing," the *wazir* replied.

The king, who was impulsive, decided to investigate. *I have my army with me. What could go wrong*? He leapt up from his chair, climbed on to his horse, and rode into the forest, leaving the *wazir* and army chiefs baffled.

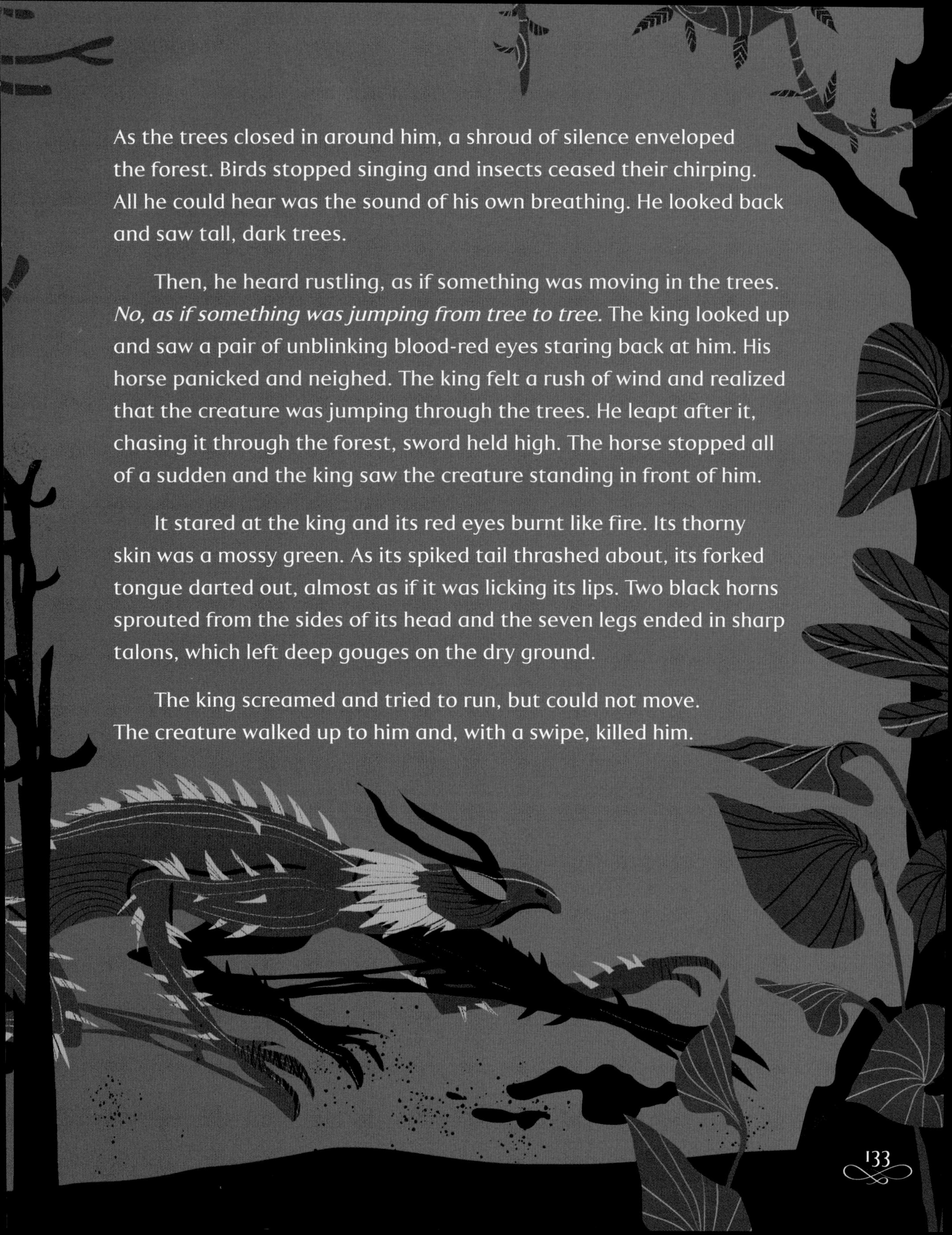

As the trees closed in around him, a shroud of silence enveloped the forest. Birds stopped singing and insects ceased their chirping. All he could hear was the sound of his own breathing. He looked back and saw tall, dark trees.

Then, he heard rustling, as if something was moving in the trees. *No, as if something was jumping from tree to tree.* The king looked up and saw a pair of unblinking blood-red eyes staring back at him. His horse panicked and neighed. The king felt a rush of wind and realized that the creature was jumping through the trees. He leapt after it, chasing it through the forest, sword held high. The horse stopped all of a sudden and the king saw the creature standing in front of him.

It stared at the king and its red eyes burnt like fire. Its thorny skin was a mossy green. As its spiked tail thrashed about, its forked tongue darted out, almost as if it was licking its lips. Two black horns sprouted from the sides of its head and the seven legs ended in sharp talons, which left deep gouges on the dry ground.

The king screamed and tried to run, but could not move. The creature walked up to him and, with a swipe, killed him.

Back in the city, the wazir grew worried. He sent out search parties that scoured the forest looking for their king, but he had vanished without a trace. They looked for eight days and then gave up. They assumed he was dead. The kingdom mourned, for despite his impulsive nature, the king was a kind man. Soon, there was no choice but to crown the young prince as the new king.

"The kingdom needs a king and it has to be you," the *wazir* told the prince. The grieving young man agreed, but first, he told the *wazir*, he had to uncover the truth behind his father's disappearance. The *wazir* begged him not to go, but the young prince was adamant.

Armed with a sharp sword and a bow with arrows, he entered the forest, much like his father had done. He stepped carefully for he knew that only a powerful creature could have bested his father who was a great warrior. He walked deeper into the forest, noticing how the birds and insects were silent, until he reached a clearing.

He stood looking at the trees, when he heard rustling and watched in horror as an unearthly creature emerged. "One, two, three ... Seven legs! What is this beast?" he whispered under his breath.

The beast circled the prince and its tail whipped out to grab and throw him to the ground. The prince leapt out of the way and shot the creature with his bow and arrow, piercing its ear. A drop of the unearthly creature's blood fell to the ground. Almost instantly, an identical beast appeared from the drop of blood. Terrified, the prince shot an arrow once again, aiming for the head, but managing only to scratch it. A drop of blood fell to the ground and yet another beast took shape. The two circled the prince, even as the first creature took on its true form. It was a shape-shifting jinn thirsty for the prince's blood.

As the creatures prepared to pounce, the prince pulled out a double-headed arrow and shot the jinn between its eyes. The evil creature fell to the ground, writhing in pain. The other beasts disappeared as if they had never been there. Before it could recover, the prince cut off the head with his sword. The jinn was slain. His father was avenged.

Exhilarated, the prince mounted the head on an arrow, placed it in a trunk, and carried it back with him to the palace. He hid it in one of the palace's 12,000 rooms. Everyone, including his mother, thought that the trunk contained great treasure, but no one knew where it was.

Soon, the prince was crowned king and, as time passed, everyone forgot about the trunk except his curious mother. She started looking for the room and searched for many nights.

One day she chanced upon a room that appeared different from the others. Its walls were grimy and the darkness within seemed to suck out her breath. She shuddered and turned to leave when she noticed a rusty trunk. As she walked towards it, she heard a voice that sounded like her husband.

"Help me," the voice said. "My dear wife, I am your husband, the king."

The queen stood there transfixed. It had been years since her husband had been killed. *This could not be him, or could it?* Distraught, she returned to her chambers, but could not forget the voice.

She found herself back in the dark room the next night. The voice spoke again, "My queen, you have returned, I knew you would come back to save me."

"Who are you?" she asked.

"I am your husband, the king. Our son killed me. He must be punished. Free me," demanded the voice.

The queen mother found herself moving towards the trunk and before she knew it, she had opened it. She peered inside and screamed. The mangled head of the evil jinn blinked back and smiled at her. "Free me," it whispered.

She screamed once again and the young king came running into the room. He shut the trunk even as the jinn whispered, “Free me.”

The young king realized how dangerous the jinn was. So, he locked the trunk and destroyed the keys. Then, he and his army took it to the very edge of the kingdom where the ocean met the land.

There, weighing it down with large rocks, they sank the trunk, so that no one may ever find it again.

When Elephants Could Fly

A myth from the Hill Saora Tribe of Odisha

There was a time when all creatures, big, medium, and small, seemed different than what they are now. The peacocks did not have trains and looked like regular birds that waddled on the ground. The elephants, however, flew everywhere. They had four giant wings, each two metres wide and they were so huge that even the great god, Kittung, flew around on one of them.

Then the world started changing. Rivers, mountains, plains, and oceans were formed and humans began building houses and settling down. Soon, the flying elephants became a nuisance.

They crowed like roosters whenever they wanted and were taller than trees. They kept flying to the sky and when they would get exhausted, flew back down and rested on rooftops. They were so heavy that the roofs would collapse and the humans would have to build their homes again, from scratch.

Sometimes, the elephants would fly up and down, just for fun, as people went about their daily business, wreaking havoc and crashing their trunks into everything. Fed up, the humans complained to Kittung, who realized that something had to be done about these naughty elephants.

One day, he called all the elephants to a massive yard for a grand feast. They came from all over – north, east, south, and west. Kittung offered them delicious food and the elephants ate so much that they had to take a nap.

While they were fast asleep, Kittung gently cut their wings, one by one. He gave one pair to the peacocks, who used them as long trains. Then, he looked around and spotted giant plantain trees that looked bare. So, he stuck the remaining wings on them, which is why today they have massive, droopy leaves.

When the elephants woke up and realized that their wings were gone, they were very, very upset.

Angry and distressed, they stormed off to the jungle, far away from the humans, where they have lived ever since.

Glossary

Appam

A sweet or savoury pancake made with fermented rice flour. This dish is popular across India.

Aravallis

One of the oldest hill systems in India that stretches from the north to the northwest.

Asura

A power-hungry mythological creature that lived underground and on earth. Not all of them a evil, but they are, at times, equated with demons.

Aza

The word for mother in Sema or Sumi, a language spoken in the state of Nagaland.

Bulrush

A very tall, grasslike marsh plant with solid stems and topped with tiny flowers.

Deva

A heavenly, divine being (or god) worshipped by Hindus.

Jeth

A summer month that extends from May to June, as per the Hindu calendar which is traditionally used in India.

Jinn

A supernatural creature from Islamic mythology and folklore.

Incarnation

The belief that souls can be reborn again and again in different forms. Many religions, such as Hinduism and Sikhism, believe in this concept.

Kafal

An edible berry with a sweet-sour flavour, which grows in the mountainous regions of northern India, Bhutan, and Nepal.

Ka Sngi

The sun and the ruler of the Blue Realm (or heaven), according to Khasi folklore.

Khasi

An indigenous ethnic group of people who are from the state of Meghalaya.

Khichdi
A dish, popular in Southeast Asian countries, made of rice and lentils.

Kittung
A local male deity of the Hill Saora tribe in Odisha. According to some myths, he is believed to be the first man on earth.

Kutki
A bitter and pungent herb, also known as picrorhiza, which is used in Ayurveda and Chinese medicine.

Lanka
The island where Ravana, the asura king, ruled according to the ancient Indian epic, Ramayana.

Naga
A mythical, partly divine snake being. It prefers staying close to waterbodies such as lakes, rivers, and oceans.

Patala lok
One of the many realms, according to Hindu mythology, located beneath the surface of the earth. Some of the other realms are heaven or swarg and earth or prithvi.

Paisa
A unit of currency in India, Nepal, and Pakistan.

Pitha
A rice cake variety that is popular in eastern states of India.

Rakshasa
A powerful being and warrior with knowledge of magic and illusion. Many of them are known to be hostile towards humans and gods.

Rebab
A medieval string instrument, which was once popular throughout Asia. The instrument resembles a lute and the sound box is made of a coconut shell.

Santal
An ethnic group who reside in India and are the largest tribe in the state of Jharkhand.

Vindhyas
A mountainous region by the ocean, according to the Ramayana. Not to be confused with the Vindhya Range.

Wazir
A high level officer or political advisor in an Islamic states. Also known as a vizier.

Bibliography

Dance of Seasons

A folk tale from Lahaul and Spiti, Himachal Pradesh, narrated by Naveen Kiran Boktapa.
Retold by Nayan Keshan

Garuda, the King of Birds

Astika Parva, The Mahabharata of Krishna-Dwaipayana Vyasa, translated into English Prose from the Original Sanskrit Text by Kisari Mohan Ganguli. Calcutta: 1883–1896.
Retold by Arushi Mathur

Guest of the Blue Realm

How the Peacock got his Beautiful Feathers, Folk-Tales of The Khasis, by KU Rafy.
London: Macmillan and Co., Limited St Martin's Street, 1920.
Retold by Ayushi Thapliyal

How Butterflies were Born

20, The Animal World, Tribal Myths of Orissa, by Verrier Elwin.
London: Oxford University Press, 1954.
Retold by Chitra Subramanyam

How to Fool an Alligator

The Alligator and the Jackal, Old Deccan Days or Hindoo Fairy Legends, Current in Southern India – Collected from Oral Tradition, by Mary Frere. London: John Murray, Albemarle Street, 1898.
Retold by Ayushi Thapliyal

How to Trick a Tiger

The Lady Tiger Slayer, The Enchanted Parrot, by the Reverend B Hale Wortham. London: Luzac & Co, 1911.
Retold by Ayushi Thapliyal

Journey Across the Ocean

A story from the Janamsakhis narrated by Gagan Dhillon Kullar.
Retold by Ayushi Thapliyal

Revenge of the Snake

Astika Parva, The Mahabharata of Krishna-Dwaipayana Vyasa, translated into English Prose from the Original Sanskrit Text by Kisari Mohan Ganguli. Calcutta: 1883–1896.
Retold by Rishi Bryan

Sir Talk-a-Lot

The Talking Turtle, The Magic Bed: A Book of East Indian Fairy-Tales, edited with an introduction by Hartwell James. Philadelphia: Henry Altemus Company, 1906.
Retold by Ayushi Thapliyal

The Clever Crab

The Cruel Crane Outwitted, The Earliest English Version of the Fables of Bidpai, "The Morall Philosophie of Doni", by Sir Thomas North, edited and induced by Joseph Jacobs, late of St. John's College, Cambridge. London: David Nutt, 1886.
Retold by Bipasha Roy

The Demon Serpent

U Thlen, The Snake Vampire, Folk-Tales of The Khasis, by KU Rafy. London: Macmillan and Co., Limited St Martin's Street, 1920.
Retold by Chitra Subramanyam

The First Eclipse

What Causes the Eclipse, Folk-Tales of The Khasis, by KU Rafy. London: Macmillan and Co., Limited St Martin's Street, 1920.
Retold by Nayan Keshan

The Grain of Corn

The Grain of Corn, Tales of the Punjab: Told by the People, by Flora Annie Steel. London: Macmillan and Co., Limited St. Martin's Street, 1910.
Retold by Ayushi Thapliyal

The Great Protector

The Bhagavata-Purana, by Jainendra Prakash Jain. Delhi: Shree Jainendra Press, 1950.
Retold by Chitra Subramanyam

The Helpful Chameleon

An oral tale passed down from generation to generation in Parsee families.
Retold by Priyanka Kharbanda

The Hungry Bear

The Bear's Bad Bargain, Tales of the Punjab: Told by the People, by Flora Annie Steel. London: Macmillan and Co., Limited St. Martin's Street, 1910.
Retold by Nayan Keshan

The Jackal's New Coat

Story Seventh, English Translation of Hitopadesha, by BT Dravid, alias Sheshadri Iyar. Bombay: Gopal Narayen & Co., Booksellers and Publishers, Second Edition, 1906.
Retold by Ayushi Thapliyal

The Light of the Firefly

Story of the Monkeys, the Firefly, and the Bird, The Katha Sarit Sagara or Ocean of the Streams of Story, Volume 2, translated by CH Tawney. Delhi: Devendra Jain for Munshiram Manoharlal, 1880.
Retold by Ayushi Thapliyal

The Matchmaker and the Leopard

A Story of the Leopard and the Marriage Broker, Santal Folk Tales, Volume III, edited by PO Bodding. Oslo: H Aschehoug & Co. (W Nygaard), 1929

Retold by Ayushi Thapliyal

The Ripe Kafal

A Garhwali folk tale narrated by Kalawati Devi.

Retold by Ayushi Thapliyal

The Saviour Spider

Al-Ankabut (The Spider), Surah 29, Quran.

Retold by Ayushi Thapliyal

The Seven-Legged Beast

The Seven-Legged Beast, Folk-Tales of Kashmir, by the Rev J Hinton Knowles. London: Kegan Paul, Trench, Trubner, & Co, First Edition, 1893.

Retold by Sukriti Kapoor

The Tiger Man

A folk tale from the Sumi tribe of Nagaland, narrated and translated by Amghali Achumi.

Retold by Arushi Mathur

The Tricksy Monkey

The Monkey with the Tom-Tom, Tales of the Sun or Folklore from the South, Collected by Mrs Howard Kingscote and Pandit Natesa Sastri. London: WH Allen & Co., 1890.

Retold by Ayushi Thapliyal

The Wily Fox

A folk tale translated from Burhi Aai'r Xaadhu, by Lakshminath Bezbarua. (Privately Printed): 1911.

Retold by Upamanyu Das

Vulture of the Vindhyas

Section LVIII, The Ramayana, Translated into English Prose from the Original Sanskrit of Valmiki, Kishkindha Kandam, Edited and Published by Manmatha Nath Dutt. Calcutta: Deva Press, 1891.

Retold by Ayushi Thapliyal

When Elephants Could Fly

72, The Animal World, Tribal Myths of Orissa, Verrier Elwin. London: Oxford University Press, 1954.

Retold by Ayushi Thapliyal

Wrath of the Witch

10, Arthropods, Myths of Middle India, by Verrier Elwin. Madras: Oxford University Press, 1949.

Retold by Ayushi Thapliyal